Hymns and Songs for Church Schools

Ruth Olson, Editor

Augsburg Publishing House

Minneapolis 15, Minnesota

HYMNS AND SONGS

FOR CHURCH SCHOOLS

Copyright © 1962 Augsburg Publishing House

Library of Congress Catalog Card No. 62-13898

Scripture quotations are from the Revised Standard Version of the Bible, copyright 1946 and 1952 by the Division of Christian Education of the National Council of Churches.

PREFACE

In compiling this hymnal it has been the desire of the publisher to present a collection of hymns that may worthily transmit the greatest hymns of our musical heritage to the children of the church. In this endeavor the publisher has had the assistance and cooperation of members of the staff of the Department of Parish Education of The American Lutheran Church, authorities on pedagogy in public school music, leaders in church music, as well as people involved in the music of the local church schools.

The selection of hymns was based on the following criteria:

1. Hymns should be consistent with our faith.

2. The emphasis should be on the praise of God—the direction, Godward.

3. The most worthy texts should be wed to most worthy tunes.

4. The child's level of comprehension and experience should be considered.

5. The tessitura should lie within the child's voice range.

6. Tunes and translations, for the most part, should be the same as used in the Lutheran Service Book and Hymnal.

7. There should be a reasonable balance in the number of hymns selected for the Sundays of the church year, festivals, and other classifications. Various national heritages should also be considered.

Many of the hymns chosen have expressed the faith of Christians of the early church, have lived through the centuries to the present day, and will live on through the children using this book. Some contemporary songs have been added with the hope that these expressions of the Spirit may also find acceptance in this and future generations.

The hymnal also includes sacred songs, songs for small children, a number of rounds, table graces, and Scripture verses set to music.

It is not the intention of the publisher that the collection of songs for small children should be considered adequate in itself. It is hoped and strongly urged that the great chorales of the church will be taught to the very young, so that the strength and virility of this heritage may also be a part of their experience. Even though they may be able to learn only one stanza or a phrase or two, they will feel they can take part in congregational singing and have the sense of belonging. As a child is subjected to and experiences only the best in music, he will appreciate and enjoy only the best.

In addition to the music sections of the book, other useful material is included: suggested opening devotions, Scripture selections, seasonal prayers, a number of Christian symbols with explanations, and annotations on certain hymns.

This is a book of praise. It is the hope and prayer of those who have contributed to its compilation that it will be a continuing source of inspiration and joy to all, especially to the children who, from these pages, learn to sing God's praise. "For great is the Lord, and greatly to be praised" (Psalm 96:4a).

THE PUBLISHER

ACKNOWLEDGMENTS

The editor gratefully acknowledges the assistance of many individuals in the preparation of this volume; especially Rev. Carl E. Fischer, for annotations on hymns, Robert P. Wetzler for explanations of symbols, Rev. Wilson Egbert, for assistance in preparing the opening devotions, and Edmund Kopietz for illustrations.

Acknowledgment is also made of the cooperation, assistance, and guidance given by Dr. Laurence N. Field, Georgia Garlid, Rev. Adam Graf, Rev. Roy Grote, Dr. Hans Knauer, Robert Larson, Betty Larson, Dr. Edwin Liemohn, Constance Lowe, Dr. O. G. Malmin, Paul Neve, Harriet Nordholm, Dr. Oscar R. Overby, Gertrude Boe Overby, Frank Pooler, Marie Pooler, Dr. Herman C. Schulz, Dr. Ellis Snyder, Rev. Johan Thorson, and Dr. C. Richard Evenson and the staff of the Department of Parish Education of The American Lutheran Church.

Copyright holders have graciously allowed the use of their hymns. Care has been taken not to infringe upon any copyrights, and it is hoped that all material has been properly credited. If there have been any oversights, due credit will be given in future editions. Special thanks are due The Commission on the Liturgy and Hymnal for permission to use many hymns from THE SERVICE BOOK AND HYMNAL.

The editor is deeply indebted to Fernanda U. Malmin, William O. Bliss, and Robert P. Wetzler for invaluable editorial assistance.

THE EDITOR

CONTENTS OF THE HYMNAL

"Behold, the Lamb of God, who takes away the sin of the world!" (John 1:29). The Lamb, signifying Christ, stands with the banner of victory.

ADVENT

Lift Up Your Heads, Ye Mighty Gates 1
TRURO. L. M.

Georg Weissel, 1590-1635
Tr. Catherine Winkworth, 1829-1878

Williams' *Psalmodia Evangelica*, 1789

With spirit

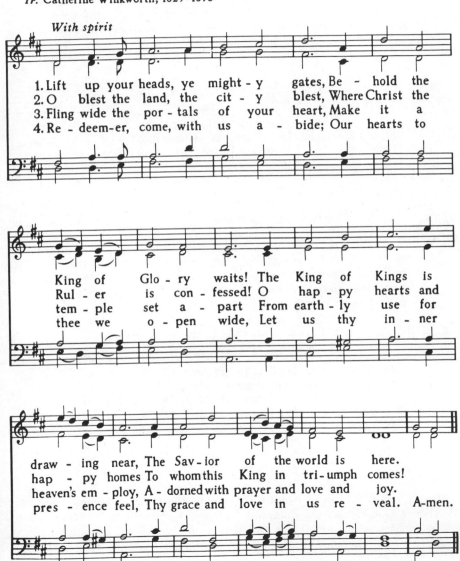

1. Lift up your heads, ye might-y gates, Be - hold the
2. O blest the land, the cit-y blest, Where Christ the
3. Fling wide the por-tals of your heart, Make it a
4. Re - deem-er, come, with us a - bide; Our hearts to

King of Glo-ry waits! The King of Kings is
Rul-er is con-fessed! O hap-py hearts and
tem-ple set a-part From earth-ly use for
thee we o-pen wide, Let us thy in-ner

draw - ing near, The Sav-ior of the world is here.
hap - py homes To whom this King in tri-umph comes!
heaven's em - ploy, A-dorned with prayer and love and joy.
pres - ence feel, Thy grace and love in us re - veal. A-men.

2 O Come, O Come, Emmanuel

VENI EMMANUEL. 88, 88, 88.

Medieval Antiphons
Latin Hymn, 1710
Tr. John M. Neale, 1818-1866

Plainsong Melody, Mode I

Flowing

1. O come, O come, Em - man - u - el, And ran-som cap - tive
2. O come, O come, thou Lord of Might, Who to thy tribes, on
3. O come, thou Rod of Jes - se, free Thine own from Sa - tan's
4. O come, thou Day-spring, come and cheer Our spir-its by thine
5. O come, thou Key of Da - vid, come, And o - pen wide our

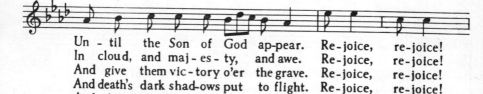

Is - ra - el, That mourns in lone - ly ex - ile here
Si - nai's height, In an - cient times didst give the law
tyr - an - ny; From depths of hell thy peo - ple save,
ad - vent here; Dis - perse the gloom - y clouds of night,
heaven-ly home; Make safe the way that leads on high,

Un - til the Son of God ap-pear. Re-joice, re-joice!
In cloud, and maj - es - ty, and awe. Re-joice, re-joice!
And give them vic - tory o'er the grave. Re-joice, re-joice!
And death's dark shad-ows put to flight. Re-joice, re-joice!
And close the path to mis - er - y. Re-joice, re-joice!

Em - man - u - el Shall come to thee, O Is - ra - el!
Em - man - u - el Shall come to thee, O Is - ra - el!
Em - man - u - el Shall come to thee, O Is - ra - el!
Em - man - u - el Shall come to thee, O Is - ra - el!
Em - man - u - el Shall come to thee, O Is - ra - el! A-men.

One of our Lord's most beautiful names is the name *Emmanuel.* As St. Matthew's Gospel tells us, *Emmanuel* means "God with us." In our daily Christian life, this is our prayer and this is our joy. When Jesus comes we have the richest blessing of all. In Jesus our Savior we have "God with us."

Come, Jesus, Holy Child, to Me

PUER NOBIS NASCITUR. L. M.

Hofgesangbuch, Leipzig, 1672
Tr. Paul Z. Strodach, 1876-1947

Composed or adapted by
Michael Praetorius, 1571-1621
Martin Shaw, 1875-1958

Brightly

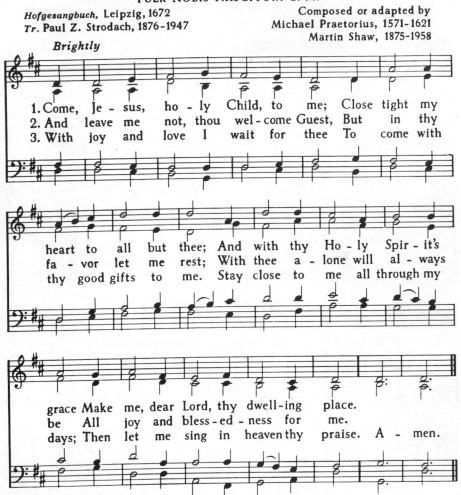

1. Come, Je - sus, ho - ly Child, to me; Close tight my heart to all but thee; And with thy Ho - ly Spir - it's grace Make me, dear Lord, thy dwell-ing place.

2. And leave me not, thou wel - come Guest, But in thy fa - vor let me rest; With thee a - lone will al - ways be All joy and bless - ed - ness for me.

3. With joy and love I wait for thee To come with thy good gifts to me. Stay close to me all through my days; Then let me sing in heaven thy praise. A - men.

Come, Jesus, Holy Child, to Me is a rich and beautiful hymn to memorize and make your own. It is a hymn you can sing and pray all through the year and all the years of your life. When you sing it with others or when you sing it by yourself you pray as St. Paul did, "that Christ may dwell in your hearts through faith" (Ephesians 3:17).

To a Virgin Meek and Mild

ADVENT

Irregular.

English version, V. E. Boe, 1872-1953
and Oscar R. Overby, 1892-

Spanish Carol
Arr. Oscar R. Overby, 1892-

In moderate time

1. To a vir-gin meek and mild Came an an-gel ho-ly,
2. By the sa-ges long fore-told, Now the day is near-ing,
3. Come in-to this heart of mine, Je-sus, guest from heav-en.

Greet-ing her, the un-de-filed, In her cham-ber low-ly;
Prom-is-es of God un-fold In the Son ap-pear-ing.
Cra-dled there, O Babe di-vine, Earth shall be a heav-en.

Hail to thee, thou bless-ed one, Chos-en moth-er of God's Son. Through a
He, the Child of Beth-le-hem, Branch di-vine of Jes-se's stem, Shall have
An-gels, sing your lull-a-by; Keep your vig-il in the sky, Till the

won-drous birth He shall come to earth, And shall reign as a
great in-crease As the Prince of Peace, And the earth shall be
dawn shall break, And all earth a-wake To pro-claim him the

King, As a King for ev-er, Je-sus, bless-ed Sav-ior.
filled With the Lord's sal-va-tion, Hope of ev-ery na-tion.
King Who shall reign for ev-er, Je-sus, bless-ed Sav-ior.

Copyright 1935, Augsburg Publishing House.

O How Shall I Receive Thee

5

ST. THEODULPH (VALET WILL ICH DIR GEBEN). 76, 76. D.

Paul Gerhardt, 1607-1676

Melchior Teschner, 1584-1635

Tr. Composite

Vigorously

1. O how shall I re - ceive thee, How greet thee, Lord, a - right?
2. Thy Zi - on palms is strew - ing, And branch - es fresh and fair;
3. Love caused thine in - car - na - tion, Love brought thee down to me;
4. Re - joice then, ye sad - heart - ed, Who sit in deep-est gloom,

All na - tions long to see thee, My hope, my heart's de - light!
My heart, its powers re - new - ing, An an - them shall pre - pare.
Thy thirst for my sal - va - tion Pro-cured my lib - er - ty.
Who mourn o'er joys de - part - ed And trem - ble at your doom,

O kin - dle, Lord most ho - ly, Thy lamp with - in my breast,
My soul puts off her sad - ness Thy glo - ries to pro - claim;
O love be - yond all tell - ing That led thee to em - brace,
He who a - lone can cheer you Is stand-ing at the door;

To do in spir - it low - ly All that may please thee best.
With all her strength and glad-ness She fain would serve thy Name.
In love all love ex - cel - ling, Our lost and fall - en race.
He brings his pit - y near you, And bids you weep no more.

6   Wake, Awake, for Night Is Flying

WACHET AUF. Irregular.

Philipp Nicolai, 1556-1608
Tr. Catherine Winkworth, 1829-1878

Philipp Nicolai, 1556-1608

Jubilantly

1. Wake, a - wake, for night is fly - ing, The watch-men on
2. Zi - on hears the watch-men sing - ing, And all her heart
3. Now let all the heavens a - dore thee, And men and an -

the heights are cry - ing, A - wake, Je - ru - sa - lem, at last!
with joy is spring-ing, She wakes, she ris - es from her gloom;
gels sing be - fore thee, With harp and cym-bal's clear-est tone;

Mid-night hears the wel-come voic - es And at the thrill-
For her Lord comes down all - glo - rious, The strong in grace,
Of one pearl each shin-ing por - tal, Where we are with

ing cry re - joic - es: Come forth, ye vir - gins, night is past!
in truth vic - to - rious, Her Star is risen, her Light is come.
the choir im - mor - tal Of an-gels round thy daz-zling throne;

The Bride-groom comes, a-wake, Your lamps with glad-ness take; Al - le - lu-ia!
Ah come, thou bless-ed One, God's own be - lov - ed Son, Al - le - lu-ia!
Nor eye hath seen, nor ear Hath yet at-tained to hear What there is ours;

And for his mar-riage feast pre-pare, For ye must go to meet him there.
We fol-low till the halls we see Where thou hast bid us sup with thee.
But we re-joice, and sing to thee Our hymn of joy e-ter-nal-ly. A-men.

Hosanna Now Through Advent 7
ST. ALBAN. 76, 76.

Claudia F. Hernaman, 1838-1898   Franz Josef Haydn, 1732-1809

Simply

1. Ho - san - na now through Ad-vent With lov-ing hearts we sing, For
2. Ho - san - na! Bless - ed Je - sus, Come in our hearts to dwell, And
3. For we who sing Ho - san - na Must like our Sav - ior be, In
4. Ho - san - na! Let this wel-come Ring out from ev - ery heart; Draw

Je - sus Christ is com-ing To be his chil-dren's King.
let our lives and voic - es Thy praise and glo - ry tell.
gen - tle - ness and meek-ness, In love and pur - i - ty.
nigh to us, O Je - sus, And nev - er-more de - part. A-men.

Prepare the Way, O Zion

8

MESSIAH. 76, 76, 77 66.

Frans M. Franzén, 1772-1847
Tr. Augustus Nelson, 1863-1949

Swedish Melody, XVII *cent.*

In stately manner

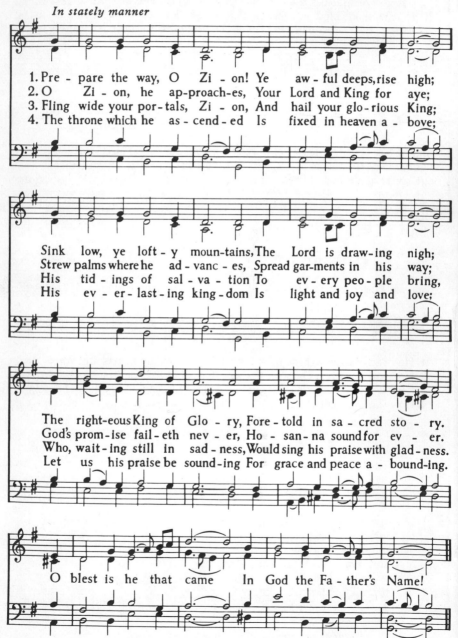

1. Pre - pare the way, O Zi - on! Ye aw - ful deeps, rise high;
2. O Zi - on, he ap-proach-es, Your Lord and King for aye;
3. Fling wide your por - tals, Zi - on, And hail your glo - rious King;
4. The throne which he as - cend - ed Is fixed in heaven a - bove;

Sink low, ye loft - y moun-tains, The Lord is draw-ing nigh;
Strew palms where he ad - vanc - es, Spread gar-ments in his way;
His tid - ings of sal - va - tion To ev - ery peo - ple bring,
His ev - er - last - ing king-dom Is light and joy and love;

The right-eous King of Glo - ry, Fore - told in sa - cred sto - ry.
God's prom-ise fail - eth nev - er, Ho - san - na sound for ev - er.
Who, wait - ing still in sad - ness, Would sing his praise with glad - ness.
Let us his praise be sound-ing For grace and peace a - bound-ing.

O blest is he that came In God the Fa - ther's Name!

Silent Night

STILLE NACHT. Irregular.

Joseph Mohr, 1792-1849

Franz Gruber, 1787-1863

Tr. unknown

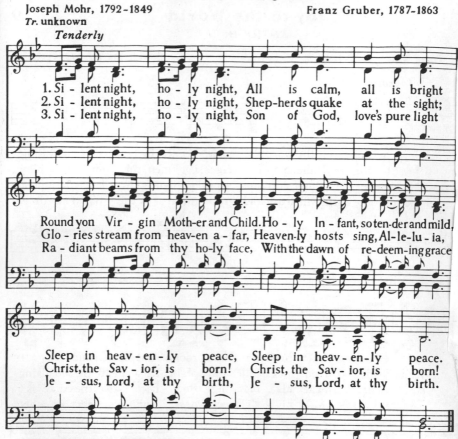

Tenderly

1. Si - lent night, ho - ly night, All is calm, all is bright
2. Si - lent night, ho - ly night, Shep-herds quake at the sight;
3. Si - lent night, ho - ly night, Son of God, love's pure light

Round yon Vir - gin Moth-er and Child. Ho - ly In - fant, so ten-der and mild,
Glo - ries stream from heav-en a - far, Heaven-ly hosts sing, Al-le-lu - ia,
Ra - diant beams from thy ho-ly face, With the dawn of re-deem-ing grace

Sleep in heav - en-ly peace, Sleep in heav - en-ly peace.
Christ, the Sav - ior, is born! Christ, the Sav - ior, is born!
Je - sus, Lord, at thy birth, Je - sus, Lord, at thy birth.

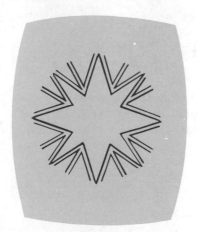

The Star of Bethlehem is often used in connection with the shepherds at Christmas. Actually, we are told of the star in the story of the Wise Men: "And lo, the star which they had seen in the East went before them, till it came to rest over the place where the child was" (Matthew 2:9).

CHRISTMAS

Joy to the World
ANTIOCH. C. M.

Isaac Watts, 1674-1748   *Arr.* Lowell Mason, 1792-1872

In moderate time

1. Joy to the world, the Lord is come! Let earth re - ceive her King;
2. Joy to the world, the Sav - ior reigns! Let men their songs em - ploy,
3. No more let sins and sor - rows grow, Nor thorns in - fest the ground;
4. He rules the world with truth and grace, And makes the na - tions prove

Let ev - ery heart pre - pare him room, And heaven and na - ture
While fields and floods, rocks, hills and plains Re - peat the sound-ing
He comes to make his bless-ings flow Far as the curse is
The glo - ries of his right-eous-ness, And won - ders of his

And

sing, And heaven and na - ture sing, And heaven, and heaven and na - ture sing.
joy, Re - peat the sound-ing joy, Re - peat, re - peat the sound-ing joy.
found, Far as the curse is found, Far as, far as the curse is found.
love, And won-ders of his love, And won - ders, won-ders of his love.

heaven and na-ture sing,   and heaven and na-ture sing,

When Christmas Morn Is Dawning

CHRISTMAS DAWN. 76, 76.

Arr. Elizabeth Ehrenborg-Posse, 1818–1880
German Folksong, 1823
Tr. Claude W. Foss, 1855–1935

Simply

1. When Christ-mas morn is dawn-ing In faith I would re - pair
2. How kind, O lov-ing Sav-ior, To come from heaven a - bove;
3. We need thee, bless-ed Je - sus, Our dear-est friend thou art;

Un - to the low-ly man-ger; My Sav - ior li - eth there,
From sin and e - vil save us, And keep us in thy love,
For - bid that we by sin - ning Should grieve thy lov-ing heart,

Un - to the low-ly man-ger; My Sav - ior li - eth there.
From sin and e - vil save us, And keep us in thy love.
For - bid that we by sin - ning Should grieve thy lov-ing heart. A-men.

After their journey from Galilee to Bethlehem, Mary and Joseph could find no place to stay. "And while they were there, the time came for her to be delivered. And she gave birth to her firstborn son and wrapped him in swaddling cloths, and laid him in a manger because there was no place for them in the inn" (Luke 2:6-7).

12

A Great and Mighty Wonder

ES IST EIN' ROS' ENTSPRUNGEN. 76, 76, 676.

St. Germanus, *cir.* 634-734
Tr. John M. Neale, 1818-1866, *alt.*

Geistliche Kirchengesäng
Cologne, 1599

In moderate time

1. A great and might-y won-der This joy-ful feast-day brings;
2. The Word be-comes in-car-nate, De-scend-ing from on high;
3. While thus they sing your Mon-arch, Those bright an-gel-ic bands,
4. Since all he comes to ran-som, By all be he a-dored,

The Vir-gin bears the In-fant, Our Lord, and King of Kings.
And cher-u-bim sing 'an-thems To shep-herds from the sky.
Re-joice, ye vales and moun-tains! Ye o-ceans, clap your hands!
The In-fant born in Beth-l'em, The Sav-ior and the Lord.

Refrain

Re-peat the hymn a-gain: 'To God on high be

glo-ry, And peace on earth to men!'

Hark, the Herald Angels Sing

13

MENDELSSOHN. 77, 77. D. With Refrain.

Charles Wesley, 1707-1788, *alt.*   Felix Mendelssohn, 1809-1847

In moderate time

1. Hark, the her - ald an - gels sing, 'Glo - ry to the new-born King;
2. Christ, by high - est heaven a - dored, Christ, the ev - er - last-ing Lord,
3. Hail, the heaven-born Prince of Peace! Hail, the Sun of Right-eous- ness!

Peace on earth, and mer-cy mild, God and sin - ners rec-on - ciled!'
Late in time be-hold him come, Off-spring of a Vir-gin's womb.
Light and life to all he brings, Risen with heal-ing in his wings.

Joy - ful, all ye na-tions, rise, Join the tri-umph of the skies,
Veiled in flesh the God-head see; Hail, the in - car-nate De - i - ty,
Mild he lays his glo-ry by, Born that man no more may die,

With the an-gel - ic host pro-claim, 'Christ is born in Beth-le - hem.'
Pleased as Man with man to dwell, Je - sus, our Im-man-u - el!
Born to raise the sons of earth, Born to give them sec-ond birth.

Hark, the her-ald an-gels sing, 'Glo-ry to the new-born King!'

14   Good Christian Men, Rejoice

IN DULCI JUBILO. Irregular.

Medieval Latin Carol   XIV *cent*. German Melody
Tr. John M. Neale, 1818-1866

Flowing

1. Good Chris-tian men, re - joice,   With heart, and soul, and voice;
2. Good Chris-tian men, re - joice,   With heart, and soul, and voice;
3. Good Chris-tian men, re - joice,   With heart, and soul, and voice;

Give ye heed to what we say: Je-sus Christ is born to-day;
Now ye hear of end-less bliss: Je-sus Christ was born for this!
Now ye need not fear the grave: Je-sus Christ was born to save!

Ox and ass be - fore him bow,   And he is in the
He hath ope'd the heaven-ly door,   And man is bless - ed
Calls you one and calls you all   To gain his ev - er -

man-ger now. Christ is born to - day!   Christ is born to - day!
ev - er-more. Christ was born for this!   Christ was born for this!
last-ing hall. Christ was born to save!   Christ was born to save!

From Heaven Above to Earth I Come   15

VOM HIMMEL HOCH. L. M.

Martin Luther, 1483-1546
Tr. Catherine Winkworth, 1829-1878

Martin Luther, 1483-1546

Flowing

1. From heaven a-bove to earth I come To bear good
2. To you this night is born a child Of Mar-y,
3. Were earth a thou-sand times as fair, Be-set with
4. Ah, dear-est Je-sus, Ho-ly Child, Make thee a
5. 'Glo-ry to God in high-est heaven, Who un-to

news to ev-ery home; Glad ti-dings of great
cho-sen moth-er mild; This lit-tle child, of
gold and jew-els rare, She yet were far too
bed, soft un-de-filed, With-in my heart, that
man his Son hath given,' While an-gels sing with

joy I bring, Where-of I now will say and sing:
low-ly birth, Shall be the joy of all the earth.
poor to be A nar-row cra-dle, Lord, to thee.
it may be A qui-et cham-ber kept for thee.
pi-ous mirth A glad new year to all the earth.

16 All Hail to Thee, O Blessed Morn

WIE SCHÖN LEUCHTET. Irregular.

Johann O. Wallin, 1779-1839
Based on German Hymn, 1621
Tr. Ernst W. Olson, 1870-1958

Philipp Nicolai, 1556-1608

With movement

1. All hail to thee, O bless-ed morn, To ti-dings long by proph-ets borne Hast thou ful-fill-ment giv-en; O sa-cred and im-mor-tal day, When un-to earth, in glo-rious ray, De-scends the grace of heav-en! Young and old their voic-es blend-ing, Praise are send-ing

2. Like oth-er men, he tears will shed, Our sor-rows share, and be our aid, Through his e-ter-nal pow-er, The love of God on us be-stow, And min-gle in our cup of woe The drops of mer-cy's show-er; Dear-ly buy-ing through his pas-sion Our sal-va-tion,

3. He comes, for our re-demp-tion sent, And by his glo-ry heaven is rent To close up-on us nev-er; Our bless-ed Shep-herd he would be, Whom we may fol-low faith-ful-ly To live with him for ev-er, Un-to realms of glo-ry wing-ing, Prais-es sing-ing

Words from the SERVICE BOOK AND HYMNAL. Used by permission.

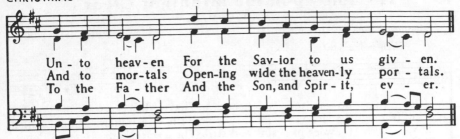

Un - to heav - en For the Sav-ior to us giv - en.
And to mor-tals Open-ing wide the heaven-ly por - tals.
To the Fa - ther And the Son, and Spir - it, ev - er.

Of the Father's Love Begotten   17
DIVINUM MYSTERIUM. 87, 87, 877.

Aurelius C. Prudentius, 348–413   XIII *cent.* Plainsong, Mode V
Tr. St.1-4, John M. Neale, 1818–1866
Tr. St.5, Henry W. Baker, 1821–1877

In moderate time

1. Of the Fa - ther's love be-got-ten Ere the worlds be-gan to be,
2. O that birth for ev - er bless-ed, When the Vir - gin, full of grace,
3. This is he whom seers in old time Chant-ed of with one ac-cord;
4. O ye heights of heav'n, a - dore him; An - gel hosts, his prais-es sing;
5. Christ, to thee, with God the Fa - ther, And, O Ho - ly Ghost, to thee,

He is Al - pha and O - me - ga, He the source, the end-ing he,
By the Ho - ly Ghost con - ceiv-ing, Bare the Sav - ior of our race;
Whom the voic - es of the proph-ets Prom-ised in their faith-ful word;
Powers, do-min-ions, bow be - fore him, And ex-tol our God and King;
Hymn and chant and high thanks-giv - ing, And un-wea-ried prais-es be:

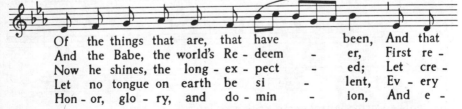

Of the things that are, that have been, And that
And the Babe, the world's Re - deem - er, First re -
Now he shines, the long - ex - pect - ed; Let cre -
Let no tongue on earth be si - lent, Ev - ery
Hon - or, glo - ry, and do - min - ion, And e -

fu - ture years shall see, Ev-er-more and ev-er - more.
vealed his sa - cred face, Ev-er-more and ev-er - more.
a - tion praise its Lord, Ev-er-more and ev-er - more.
voice in con-cert ring, Ev-er-more and ev-er - more.
ter - nal vic - to - ry, Ev-er-more and ev-er - more. A - men.

It Came upon the Midnight Clear

CAROL. C. M. D.

Edmund H. Sears, 1810-1876

Richard S. Willis, 1819-1900

With movement

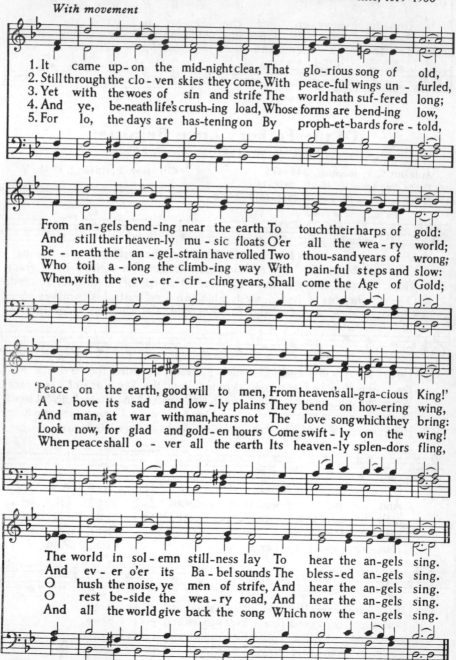

1. It came up-on the mid-night clear, That glo-rious song of old,
2. Still through the clo - ven skies they come, With peace-ful wings un - furled,
3. Yet with the woes of sin and strife The world hath suf-fered long;
4. And ye, be-neath life's crush-ing load, Whose forms are bend-ing low,
5. For lo, the days are has-tening on By proph-et-bards fore - told,

From an - gels bend-ing near the earth To touch their harps of gold:
And still their heaven-ly mu - sic floats O'er all the wea - ry world;
Be - neath the an - gel-strain have rolled Two thou-sand years of wrong;
Who toil a - long the climb-ing way With pain-ful steps and slow:
When, with the ev - er - cir - cling years, Shall come the Age of Gold;

'Peace on the earth, good will to men, From heaven's all-gra-cious King!'
A - bove its sad and low - ly plains They bend on hov-ering wing,
And man, at war with man, hears not The love song which they bring:
Look now, for glad and gold-en hours Come swift - ly on the wing!
When peace shall o - ver all the earth Its heaven-ly splen-dors fling,

The world in sol - emn still-ness lay To hear the an-gels sing.
And ev - er o'er its Ba - bel sounds The bless-ed an-gels sing.
O hush the noise, ye men of strife, And hear the an-gels sing.
O rest be-side the wea - ry road, And hear the an-gels sing.
And all the world give back the song Which now the an-gels sing.

Angels We Have Heard on High

GLORIA. 77, 77. With Refrain.

Traditional French Carol
Alt. Earl Marlatt, 1892-

French Carol
Arr. Edward S. Barnes, 1887-

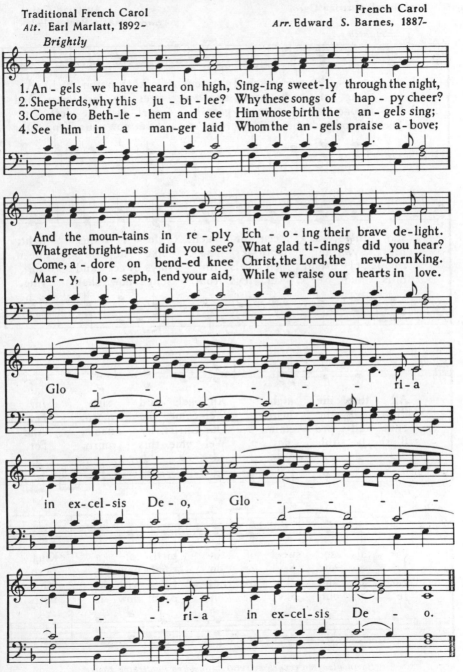

Brightly

1. An-gels we have heard on high, Sing-ing sweet-ly through the night,
2. Shep-herds, why this ju-bi-lee? Why these songs of hap-py cheer?
3. Come to Beth-le-hem and see Him whose birth the an-gels sing;
4. See him in a man-ger laid Whom the an-gels praise a-bove;

And the moun-tains in re-ply Ech-o-ing their brave de-light.
What great bright-ness did you see? What glad ti-dings did you hear?
Come, a-dore on bend-ed knee Christ, the Lord, the new-born King.
Mar-y, Jo-seph, lend your aid, While we raise our hearts in love.

Glo - - - - - ri-a in ex-cel-sis De-o, Glo - - - - - ri-a in ex-cel-sis De-o.

As Lately We Watched

Irregular.

Traditional Austrian Carol

Austrian Carol
Harm. Marie Pooler, 1928-

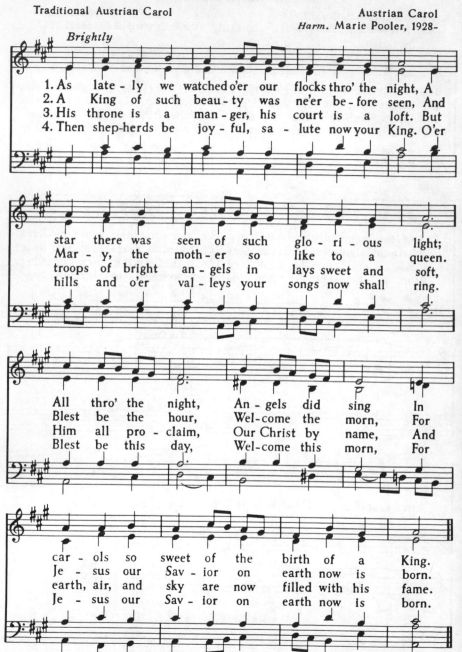

1. As late-ly we watched o'er our flocks thro' the night, A
2. A King of such beau-ty was ne'er be-fore seen, And
3. His throne is a man-ger, his court is a loft. But
4. Then shep-herds be joy-ful, sa-lute now your King. O'er

star there was seen of such glo-ri-ous light;
Mar-y, the moth-er so like to a queen.
troops of bright an-gels in lays sweet and soft,
hills and o'er val-leys your songs now shall ring.

All thro' the night, An-gels did sing In
Blest be the hour, Wel-come the morn, For
Him all pro-claim, Our Christ by name, And
Blest be this day, Wel-come this morn, For

car-ols so sweet of the birth of a King.
Je-sus our Sav-ior on earth now is born.
earth, air, and sky are now filled with his fame.
Je-sus our Sav-ior on earth now is born.

Harmonization copyright 1960, Augsburg Publishing House.

O Come, All Ye Children

IHR KINDERLEIN, KOMMET. 11 11, 11 11.

Christian v. Schmid, 1768-1854
Johann A. P. Schulz, 1747-1800
Tr. Anonymous

1. O come, all ye chil - dren, O come, one and all,
To Beth - le - hem haste, to the man - ger so small,
God's Son for a gift has been sent you this night
To be your Re - deem - er, your Joy and De - light.

2. He's born in a sta - ble for you and for me,
Draw near by the bright gleam-ing star - light to see,
In swad-dling clothes ly - ing, so meek and so mild,
And pur - er than an - gels, the heav - en - ly Child.

3. See Mar - y and Jo - seph with love - beam-ing eyes
Are gaz - ing up - on the rude bed where he lies,
The shep-herds are kneel - ing, with hearts full of love,
While an - gels sing loud Al - le - lu - ias a - bove.

4. Kneel down and a - dore him with shep-herds to - day,
Lift up lit - tle hands now, and praise him as they;
Re - joice that a Sav - ior from sin you can boast,
And join in the song of the heav - en - ly host. A-men.

5. Dear Christ Child, what gifts can we children bestow
By which our affection and gladness to show?
No riches and treasures of value can be,
But hearts that believe are accepted with thee.

6. Our hearts, then, to thee we will offer today,
We offer them gladly, accept them, we pray,
And make them so spotless and pure that we may
Abide in thy presence in heaven for aye.

AWAY IN A MANGER. 11 11, 11 11.

St. 1-2, Anonymous

St. 3, John T. McFarland, 1851-1913

XIX *cent.* American

FIRST TUNE

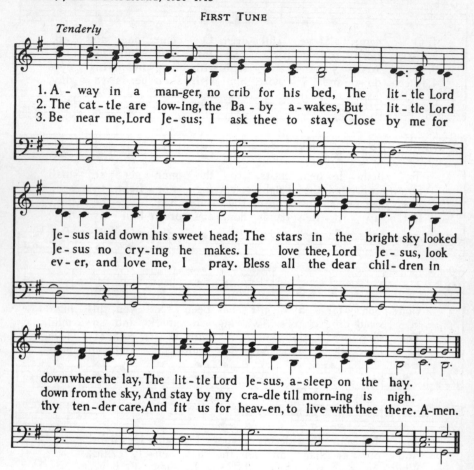

1. A - way in a man-ger, no crib for his bed, The lit - tle Lord
2. The cat - tle are low - ing, the Ba - by a - wakes, But lit - tle Lord
3. Be near me, Lord Je - sus; I ask thee to stay Close by me for

Je - sus laid down his sweet head; The stars in the bright sky looked
Je - sus no cry - ing he makes. I love thee, Lord Je - sus, look
ev - er, and love me, I pray. Bless all the dear chil - dren in

down where he lay, The lit - tle Lord Je - sus, a - sleep on the hay.
down from the sky, And stay by my cra - dle till morn - ing is nigh.
thy ten - der care, And fit us for heav - en, to live with thee there. A - men.

From earliest childhood we sing this "picture-song" of Christmas. Each time we sing it we see Jesus—the Son of God who became man, the Son of God born of Mary—in all the lowliness and weakness of infancy, like us in every way and yet without sin.

But in *Away in a Manger* we also see Jesus as he *now* is: our risen, living Lord—the Son of God, our Savior—the Son of God, our King—our Savior-King through whom God gives us the forgiveness of sins, life, and salvation.

Away in a Manger

CRADLE SONG. 11 11, 11 11.

St. 1-2. Anonymous
St. 3. John T. McFarland, 1851-1913

William J. Kirkpatrick, 1838-1921
Harm. Ralph Vaughan Williams, 1872-1958

SECOND TUNE

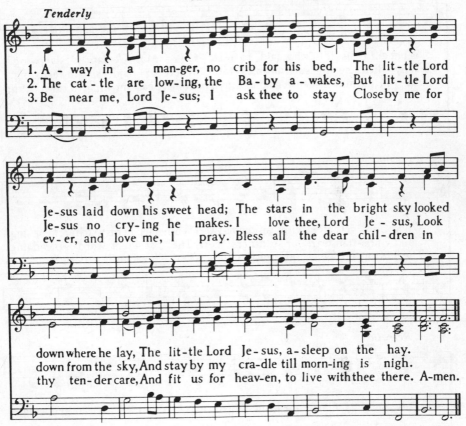

Tenderly

1. A - way in a man-ger, no crib for his bed, The lit-tle Lord
2. The cat-tle are low-ing, the Ba - by a - wakes, But lit-tle Lord
3. Be near me, Lord Je-sus; I ask thee to stay Close by me for

Je-sus laid down his sweet head; The stars in the bright sky looked
Je-sus no cry-ing he makes. I love thee, Lord Je - sus, Look
ev-er, and love me, I pray. Bless all the dear chil-dren in

down where he lay, The lit-tle Lord Je-sus, a-sleep on the hay.
down from the sky, And stay by my cra-dle till morn-ing is nigh.
thy ten-der care, And fit us for heav-en, to live with thee there. A-men.

Harmonization from SONGS OF PRAISE, ENLARGED EDITION, *by permission of Oxford University Press.*

Martin Luther spoke of Jesus as "a strange sort of a king." And it is strange, is it not, that there was no room in the inn, no crib for his bed, when King Jesus was born?

But this reminds us again and again how great a king our Lord Jesus is. Here we see that he came not to command or to conquer. Instead he came to save and to bless, to win us by his love, and to receive us into his kingdom now and for evermore.

What Child Is This

GREENSLEEVES. 87, 87. With Refrain.

William C. Dix, 1837-1898

English, before 1642

In moderate time

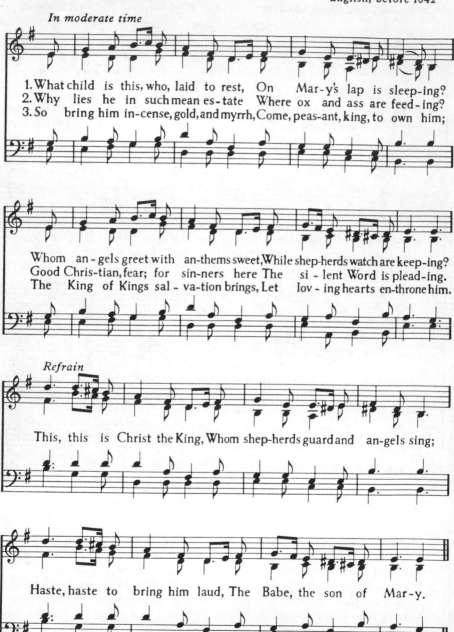

1. What child is this, who, laid to rest, On Mar-y's lap is sleep-ing?
2. Why lies he in such mean es-tate Where ox and ass are feed-ing?
3. So bring him in-cense, gold, and myrrh, Come, peas-ant, king, to own him;

Whom an-gels greet with an-thems sweet, While shep-herds watch are keep-ing?
Good Chris-tian, fear; for sin-ners here The si-lent Word is plead-ing.
The King of Kings sal-va-tion brings, Let lov-ing hearts en-throne him.

Refrain

This, this is Christ the King, Whom shep-herds guard and an-gels sing;

Haste, haste to bring him laud, The Babe, the son of Mar-y.

Hark, Now, O Shepherds

KOMMET IHR HIRTEN. Irregular.

English version,
Cordelia B. Fenno

Czechoslovakian Carol
Harm. Marie Pooler, 1928-

Brightly

1. Hark, now, O shep-herds, great news do we bring!
2. See now in beau-ty, sweet Moth-er and Child!
3. An-gels bright shin-ing, great ti-dings you bring,

Might-y the mon-arch whose prais-es we sing.
God's ten-der light o'er them glow-ing yet mild.
News of sweet Mar-y and Je-sus, our King,

Lo, in the man-ger lies Je-sus ho-ly, Son of the gen-tle
O'er all the world the star, bright-ly beam-ing, Soft sheds its lov-ing
Straight will we jour-ney forth, glad-ly bring-ing All our de-vo-tion

maid, Mar-y low-ly, Shep-herds re-joice!
rays, gent-ly stream-ing, Shep-herds re-joice!
fer-vent-ly sing-ing, Christ now is born!

Infant Holy, Infant Lowly

W ZLOBIE LEZY. Irregular.

Polish Carol
Para. Edith M.G. Reed, 1885–1933

Polish Carol
Harm. David H. Jones, 1953

Simply

1. In-fant ho-ly, In-fant low-ly, For his bed a cat-tle stall; Ox-en low-ing, Lit-tle know-ing Christ the Babe is Lord of all. Swift are wing-ing, An-gels sing-ing, No-els ring-ing, Ti-dings bring-ing: Christ the Babe is Lord of all.

2. Flocks were sleep-ing; Shep-herds keep-ing Vig-il till the morn-ing new Saw the glo-ry, Heard the sto-ry, Ti-dings of a gos-pel true. Thus re-joic-ing, Free from sor-row, Prais-es voic-ing Greet the mor-row: Christ the Babe was born for you.

O Come, All Ye Faithful

ADESTE FIDELES. Irregular.

Latin Hymn, XVIII *cent.*
Tr. Frederick Oakeley, 1802-1880,
and others

Wade's *Cantus diversi*, 1751

In moderate time

1. O come, all ye faith - ful, joy - ful and tri - um - phant, O come ye, O come ye to Beth - le - hem! Come and be - hold him, born the King of an - gels:

2. Sing, choirs of an - gels, sing in ex - ul - ta - tion, O sing, all ye cit - i-zens of heaven a - bove! Glo - ry to God, all glo - ry in the high - est:

3. Yea, Lord, we greet thee, born this hap - py morn - ing, O Je - sus, to thee be all glo - ry given; Word of the Fa - ther, now in flesh ap - pear - ing:

Refrain

O come, let us a - dore him, O come, let us a - dore him, O come, let us a - dore him, Christ, the Lord!

27   O Little Town of Bethlehem

ST. LOUIS. 86, 86, 76, 86.

Phillips Brooks, 1835-1893   Lewis H. Redner, 1831-1908

Quietly

1. O   lit - tle town of Beth - le - hem, How still we see thee   lie!
2. For Christ is born of Mar - y, And gath-ered all   a - bove,
3. How si - lent-ly, how si - lent-ly, The won-drous Gift is given!
4. O   ho - ly Child of Beth - le - hem, De - scend to us, we pray;

A - bove thy deep and dream-less sleep The si - lent stars go by;
While mor-tals sleep, the an - gels keep Their watch of won-dering love.
So   God im-parts to hu - man hearts The bless-ings of his heaven.
Cast out our sin, and en - ter in, Be born in us to - day.

Yet   in thy dark streets shin - eth The ev - er - last - ing Light;
O   morn-ing stars, to - geth - er Pro - claim the ho - ly birth,
No   ear may hear his com - ing, But in this world of sin,
We   hear the Christ-mas an - gels The great glad ti - dings tell;

The hopes and fears of all the years Are met in thee to - night.
And prais-es sing to God the King, And peace to men on earth!
Where meek souls will re-ceive him, still The dear Christ en-ters in.
O   come to us, a - bide with us, Our Lord Im - man-u - el! A-men.

Beside Thy Manger Here I Stand

28

ICH STEH AN DEINER KRIPPEN HIER. 87, 87, 887.

From the German
Tr. John Troutbeck, 1832-1899

From *The Christmas Oratorio*
J. S. Bach, 1685-1750

Tenderly

Be - side thy man - ger here I stand, O thou that ev - er liv - est, And bring thee with a will - ing hand The ver - y gifts thou giv - est. Ac - cept me; 'tis my mind and heart, My soul, my strength, my ev - ery part, That thou from me re - quir - est. A - men.

29
All My Heart This Night Rejoices
WARUM SOLLT' ICH. 8, 33, 6. D.

Paul Gerhardt, 1607-1676
Johann G. Ebeling, 1637-1676
Tr. Catherine Winkworth, 1829-1878

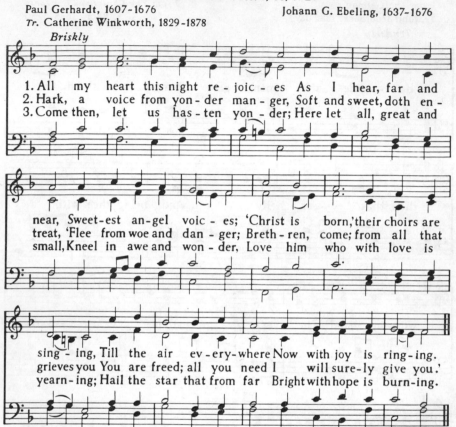

Briskly

1. All my heart this night re - joic - es As I hear, far and
2. Hark, a voice from yon - der man - ger, Soft and sweet, doth en -
3. Come then, let us has - ten yon - der; Here let all, great and

near, Sweet-est an-gel voic - es; 'Christ is born,'their choirs are
treat, 'Flee from woe and dan - ger; Breth-ren, come; from all that
small, Kneel in awe and won - der, Love him who with love is

sing - ing, Till the air ev - ery-where Now with joy is ring-ing.
grieves you You are freed; all you need I will sure-ly give you.'
yearn - ing; Hail the star that from far Bright with hope is burn-ing.

Three crowns and a star are used to remind us of the Wise Men. "Now when Jesus was born in Bethlehem of Judea in the days of Herod the king, behold wise men from the East came to Jerusalem, saying, 'Where is he who has been born king of the Jews? For we have seen his star in the East, and have come to worship him'" (Matthew 2:1-2). The Bible doesn't tell us much about the Wise Men. Through the years the idea has grown that they were three in number and that they were kings as well.

Thy Little Ones, Dear Lord, Are We 30

PAEDIA. L. M.

Hans A. Brorson, 1694-1764
Tr. Harriet R. K. Spaeth, 1845-1925

Johann A. P. Schulz, 1747-1800

1. Thy lit - tle ones, dear Lord, are we, And come thy low - ly bed to see; En - light - en ev - ery soul and mind, That we the way to thee may find.

2. With songs we has - ten thee to greet, And kiss the dust be - fore thy feet; O bless - ed hour, O sweet-est night, That gave thee birth, our soul's de - light.

3. O draw us whol - ly to thee, Lord. Do thou to us thy grace ac - cord, True faith and love to us im - part, That we may hold thee in our heart.

4. Un - til at last we too pro - claim With all thy saints, thy glo - rious Name; In par - a - dise our songs re - new, And praise thee as the an - gels do. A-men.

How long do you celebrate Christmas?

Today in America we have most of our Christmas festivities weeks before Christmas. Then Christmas comes . . . suddenly Christmas is over . . . and it's back to school or to work as usual.

Hymn No. 28, *Beside Thy Manger*, comes from a time when Christmas Day was the beginning and not the end of the Christmas season. In those days Christmas continued with church services, family festivities, and visiting all during the week *after* Christmas . . . and then into the first full week of the new year. Even though this is not our custom today, you can carry the Gospel of Christmas with you into the new year—with the prayers you pray when you sing *Beside Thy Manger*.

31 While by My Sheep I Watched at Night

Irregular.

English version,
Theodore Baker, 1851-1934

XVII *cent.* German Carol
Harm. Marie Pooler, 1928-

1. While by my sheep I watched at night, Glad ti-dings brought an an-gel bright:
2. There shall be born, so he did say, In Beth-le-hem a child to-day:
3. There shall he lie in man-ger mean, Who shall re-deem the world from sin:
4. Lord, ev-er-more to me be nigh, Then shall my heart be filled with joy!

How great my joy, great my joy, joy, joy, joy, joy, joy, joy, joy! Praise we the Lord in heaven on high. Praise we the Lord in heaven on high.

A few voices may be selected to sing the "Echo" parts.
Harmonization copyright 1960, Augsburg Publishing House.

The First Noel

THE FIRST NOWELL. Irregular. With Refrain.

Traditional English Carol   Traditional English Carol

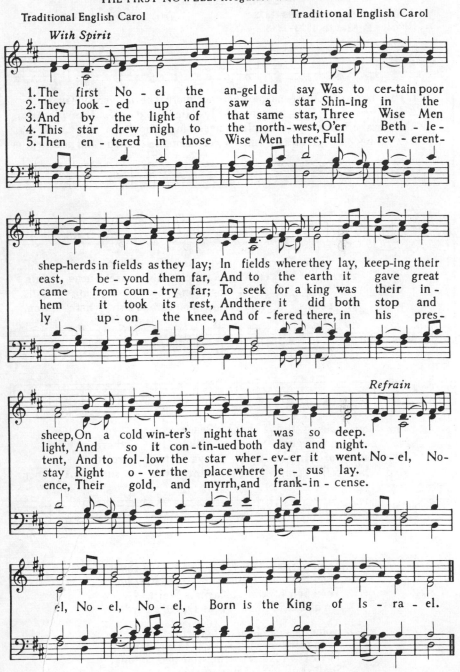

With Spirit

1. The first No - el the an-gel did say Was to cer-tain poor
2. They look - ed up and saw a star Shin-ing in the
3. And by the light of that same star, Three Wise Men
4. This star drew nigh to the north-west, O'er Beth - le -
5. Then en - tered in those Wise Men three, Full rev - erent-

shep-herds in fields as they lay; In fields where they lay, keep-ing their
east, be - yond them far, And to the earth it gave great
came from coun - try far; To seek for a king was their in -
hem it took its rest, And there it did both stop and
ly up - on the knee, And of - fered there, in his pres -

Refrain

sheep, On a cold win-ter's night that was so deep.
light, And so it con - tin-ued both day and night.
tent, And to fol - low the star wher - ev-er it went. No - el, No -
stay Right o - ver the place where Je - sus lay.
ence, Their gold, and myrrh, and frank - in - cense.

el, No - el, No - el, Born is the King of Is - ra - el.

33 The Happy Christmas Comes Once More

EMMANUEL. L. M.

Nikolai F. S. Grundtvig, 1783-1872
Tr. Charles P. Krauth, 1823-1883

Carl C. N. Balle, 1806-1855

Joyfully

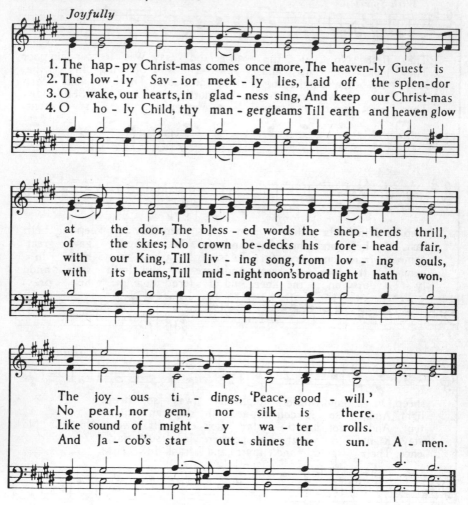

1. The hap-py Christ-mas comes once more, The heaven-ly Guest is
2. The low-ly Sav-ior meek-ly lies, Laid off the splen-dor
3. O wake, our hearts, in glad-ness sing, And keep our Christ-mas
4. O ho-ly Child, thy man-ger gleams Till earth and heaven glow

at the door, The bless-ed words the shep-herds thrill,
of the skies; No crown be-decks his fore-head fair,
with our King, Till liv-ing song, from lov-ing souls,
with its beams, Till mid-night noon's broad light hath won,

The joy-ous ti-dings, 'Peace, good-will.'
No pearl, nor gem, nor silk is there.
Like sound of might-y wa-ter rolls.
And Ja-cob's star out-shines the sun. A-men.

5. Thou patriarchs' joy, thou prophets' song,
   Thou heavenly Dayspring, looked for long,
   Thou Son of Man, Incarnate Word,
   Great David's Son, great David's Lord:

6. Come, Jesus, glorious heavenly Guest,
   Keep thine own Christmas in our breast,
   Then David's harpstrings, hushed so long,
   Shall swell our jubilee of song.

I Am So Glad Each Christmas Eve

CHRISTMAS EVE. C. M.

Marie Wexelsen, 1832-1911
Tr. Peter A. Sveeggen, 1881-

Peder Knudsen, 1819-1863

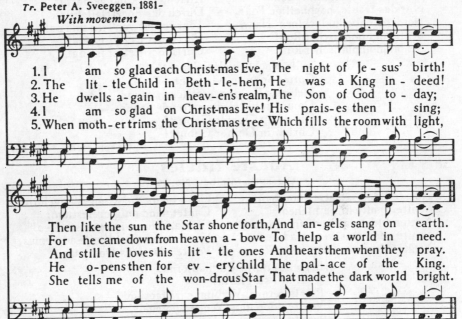

1. I am so glad each Christ-mas Eve, The night of Je - sus' birth!
2. The lit - tle Child in Beth - le-hem, He was a King in - deed!
3. He dwells a-gain in heav-en's realm,The Son of God to - day;
4. I am so glad on Christ-mas Eve! His prais-es then I sing;
5. When moth-er trims the Christ-mas tree Which fills the room with light,

Then like the sun the Star shone forth,And an-gels sang on earth.
For he came down from heaven a - bove To help a world in need.
And still he loves his lit - tle ones And hears them when they pray.
He o-pens then for ev - ery child The pal - ace of the King.
She tells me of the won-drous Star That made the dark world bright.

6. She says the Star is shining still,
And never will grow dim;
And if it shines upon my way,
It leads me up to him.

7. And so I love each Christmas Eve
And I love Jesus, too;
And that he loves me every day
I know so well is true.

Jeg er saa glad 35

Norwegian (Melody No. 34)

1. Jeg er saa glad hver julekveld;
ti da blev Jesus født,
da lyste stjernen som en sol,
og engle sang saa sødt.

2. Det lille barn i Betlehem;
han var en konge stor,
som kom fra himlens høie slot
ned til vor arme jord.

3. Nu bor han vel i himmerik,
han er Guds egen søn,
men husker altid paa de smaa
og hører deres bøn.

4. Jeg er saa glad hver julekveld
da synger vi hans pris,
da aapner han for alle smaa
sit søde paradis.

Marie Wexelsen, 1832-1911

När juldagsmorgon glimmar 36

Swedish (Melody No. 11)

1. När juldagsmorgon glimmar,
Jag vill till stallet gå,
Der Gud i nattens timmar
Re'n hvilar uppå strå.

2. Hur god du var, som ville
Till jorden komma ner!
Nu ej i synd jag spille
Min barndoms dagar mer!

3. Dig, Jesus, vi behöfva,
Du käre barnavän!
Jag vill ej mer bedröfva
Med synder dig igen!

Arr. Elizabeth Ehrenborg-Posse, 1818-1880

37   Stille Nacht, heilige Nacht
German (Melody No. 10)

1. Stille Nacht, heilige Nacht!
Alles schläft, einsam wacht
Nur das traute, hochheilige Paar.
Holder Knabe im lockigen Haar,
Schlaf in himmlischer Ruh!
Schlaf in himmlischer Ruh!

2. Stille Nacht, heilige Nacht!
Hirten erst kund gemacht;
Durch der Engel Hallelujah
Tönt es laut von fern und nah:
Christ der Retter ist da!
Christ der Retter ist da!

3. Stille Nacht, heilige Nacht!
Gottes Sohn, o wie lacht
Lieb aus Deinem göttlichen Mund
Da uns schlägt die rettende Stund,
Christ, in Deiner Geburt!
Christ, in Deiner Geburt!

Joseph Mohr, 1792-1849

38   Adeste fideles
Old Latin (Melody No. 26)

1. Adeste fideles, laeti triumphantes;
Venite, venite in Bethlehem.
Natum videte, Regem angelorum:
Venite adoremus, Venite adoremus,
Venite adoremus Dominum.

2. Cantet nunc Io! Chorus angelorum;
Cantet nunc aula coelestium:
Gloria, Gloria in excelsis Deo!
Venite adoremus, Venite adoremus,
Venite adoremus Dominum.

3. Ergo qui natus die hodierna,
Jesu, tibi sit gloria!
Patris æterni Verbum caro factum!
Venite adoremus, Venite adoremus,
Venite adoremus Dominum.

39   Vom Himmel hoch da komm' ich her
German (Melody No. 12)

1. Vom Himmel hoch da komm' ich her,
Ich bring' euch gute neue Mär,
Der guten Mär bring' ich so viel,
Davon ich sing'n und sagen will.

2. Euch ist ein Kindlein heut' gebor'n
Von einer Jungfrau auserkor'n
Ein Kindelein so zart und fein,
Das soll eu'r Freud' und Wonne sein.

3. Lob, Ehr sei Gott im höchsten Thron,
Der uns schenkt Seinen ein'gen Sohn,
Des freuet sich der Engel Schar
Und singet uns solch neues Jahr.

Martin Luther, 1483-1546

40   Her kommer dine arme smaa
Norwegian (Melody No. 30)

1. Her kommer dine arme smaa,
o Jesus, i din stald at gaa,
oplys enhver i sjel og sind,
at finde veien til dig ind!

2. Vi løper dig med sang imot,
og kysser støvet for din fot;
o salig stund, o søte nat,
da du blev født, vor sjeleskat!

3. Saa drag os ganske til dig hen,
du store, milde sjeleven,
saa vi i troen favner dig
og følger paa din himmelvei!

4. Her staar vi nu i flok og rad
om dig, vort skjønne hjerteblad,
ak hjelp at vi og alle maa
i himlen for din trone staa!

Hans A. Brorson, 1694-1764

O How Beautiful the Sky

41

CELESTIA. 77, 88, 77.

Nikolai F. S. Grundtvig, 1783-1872
Tr. Ingebret Dorrum, 1877-1952

Danish Melody

Brightly

1. O how beau-ti - ful the sky, With the spark-ling stars on high,
2. In the midst of Christ-mas night, While the stars were shin-ing bright,
3. Long a - go it was fore-told By God's chos - en men of old,
4. Wise Men by this Star were led To the Christ-child's low-ly bed.
5. In his Word did God pro-vide Such a star to be our guide.

How they glit-ter, bright-ly gleam-ing, How they twin-kle, glad-some, beam-ing,
Of a sud-den, clear and ra-diant, One ap-peared and shone re-splend-ent
When at mid-night such a won-der Did ap-pear in heaven up yon - der,
Guid-ing Star, O may we heed thee, May we know we ev - er need thee,
Ho - ly Writ, the Gos-pel sto - ry, Doth re-veal to us the glo - ry,

As they draw our hearts to heaven, As they draw our hearts to heaven.
With the lus-ter of the sun, With the lus-ter of the sun.
Born should be a Sav - ior King, Born should be a Sav - ior King.
Lead us to our heaven-ly King, Lead us to our heaven-ly King.
Lead - ing on-ward, on to Christ, Lead - ing on-ward, on to Christ.

From THE CONCORDIA HYMNAL, *copyright Augsburg Publishing House.*

Deilig er den Himmel blaa

42

1. Deilig er den Himmel blaa,
Lyst det er at se derpaa,
Hvor de gyldne Stjerner blinke,
Hvor de smile, hvor de vinke,
Os fra Jorden op til sig,
Os fra Jorden op til sig.

2. Det var midt i Jule-Nat,
Hver en Stjerne glimted mat,
Men med Et der blev at skue,
En saa klar paa Himlens Bue,
Som en lille Stjernesol.
Som en lille Stjernesol.

3. Vise Mænd fra Østerland
Drog i Verden ud paa Stand,
For den Konge at oplede,
For den Konge at tilbede,
Som var født i samme Stund,
Som var født i samme Stund.

Nikolai F. S. Grundtvig, 1783-1872

(Danish)

43 How Brightly Beams the Morning Star

WIE SCHÖN LEUCHTET. Irregular.

Philipp Nicolai, 1556-1608
Tr. *Service Book and Hymnal,* 1955

Philipp Nicolai, 1556-1608

With movement

1. How bright-ly beams the morn-ing star! What sud-den
2. Through thee a - lone can we be blest; Then deep be
3. All praise to him who came to save, Who con-quered

ra - diance from a - far Doth cheer us with its shin - ing?
on our hearts im-pressed The love that thou hast borne us;
death and scorned the grave; Each day new praise re - sound-eth

Bright-ness of God, that breaks our night And fills the
So make us read - y to ful - fill With ar - dent
To him, the Life who once was slain, The Friend whom

dark-ened souls with light, Who long for truth were pin - ing!
zeal thy ho - ly will, Though men may vex or scorn us;
none shall trust in vain, Whose grace for aye a - bound-eth;

New - ly, tru - ly, God's Word feeds us, Right - ly leads us,
Hold us, fold us, lest we fail thee, Lo, we hail thee,
Sing then, ring then, tell the sto - ry Of his glo - ry,

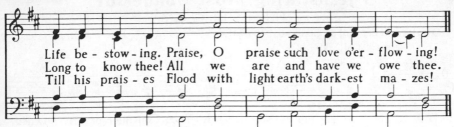

Life be - stow - ing. Praise, O praise such love o'er - flow - ing!
Long to know thee! All we are and have we owe thee.
Till his prais - es Flood with light earth's dark-est ma - zes!

For another arrangement of music, see No. 16.

As with Gladness Men of Old   44
DIX. (TREUER HEILAND.) 77, 77, 77.

William C. Dix, 1837-1898   Conrad Kocher, 1786-1872

In moderate time

1. As with glad - ness men of old Did the guid-ing Star be - hold;
2. As with joy - ful steps they sped To that low - ly man-ger - bed,
3. As they of - fered gifts most rare At that man-ger rude and bare;
4. Ho-ly Je - sus, ev - ery day Keep us in the nar - row way;
5. In the heaven-ly coun-try bright Need they no cre - a - ted light;

As with joy they hailed its light, Lead - ing on-ward, beam-ing bright;
There to bend the knee be-fore Him whom heaven and earth a - dore;
So may we with ho - ly joy, Pure and free from sin's al - loy,
And, when earth-ly things are past, Bring our ran-somed souls at last
Thou its light, its joy, its crown, Thou its sun which goes not down;

So, most gra-cious God, may we Ev - er-more be led to thee.
So may we with will - ing feet Ev - er seek thy mer - cy-seat.
All our cost-liest treas-ures bring, Christ, to thee, our heaven-ly King.
Where they need no star to guide, Where no clouds thy glo - ry hide.
There for ev - er may we sing Al - le - lu - ias to our King. A-men.

45   O Jesus, King Most Wonderful

WINCHESTER. C. M.

Ascribed to Bernard of Clairvaux, 1091-1153
Tr. Edward Caswall, 1814-1878

Este's *Psalter*, 1592

In moderate time

1. O   Je - sus, King most won-der-ful,   Thou Con-quer-or   re - nowned,
2. When once thou vis - it - est the heart, Then truth be-gins to   shine,
3. O   Je - sus, light of   all be-low, Thou fount of life and   fire,
4. May   ev - ery heart con - fess thy Name, And   ev - er thee a - dore,
5. Thee   may our tongues for   ev - er bless; Thee may we love a - lone,

Thou sweet-ness most in - ef - fa - ble, In   whom all joys are   found!
Then earth - ly van - i - ties de-part, Then kin-dles love di - vine.
Sur - pass-ing all the joys we know, All   that we can de - sire;
And, seek - ing thee, it - self in-flame To   seek thee more and more.
And   ev - er in our lives ex-press The im - age of thine own. A-men.

Have you ever noticed the close connection between the great festivals of the Church Year and the second article of the Apostles' Creed?

Christmas and Epiphany ring in our minds each time we confess "I believe . . . in Jesus Christ his only Son our Lord . . . conceived by the Holy Ghost, Born of the Virgin Mary."

Next, the whole Gospel of Lent and Holy Week unfolds before us as we say, "Suffered under Pontius Pilate, was crucified, dead and buried."

Then we come to the ringing shouts of Easter and Ascensiontide: "The third day he rose again from the dead; He ascended into heaven."

Finally we look from time to eternity. We confess our hope and expectation for life everlasting when Christ "shall come to judge the quick and the dead."

> Glory be to the Father, and to the Son, and to the
> Holy Ghost: as it was in the beginning, is now, and
> ever shall be, world without end. Amen.

O Lamb of God

O LAMM GOTTES. 77, 77, 777.

Nikolaus Decius, d. 1541
Tr. Arthur T. Russell, 1806-1874, alt.

Nikolaus Decius, d. 1541

46

Slowly

St. 1, 2, 3.

O Lamb of God most ho - ly! Who on the Cross didst suf - fer, And pa-tient still and low - ly, Thy - self to scorn didst of - fer; Our sins by thee were tak - en, Or hope had us for-sak - en:

St. 1, 2.
Have mer - cy on us, Je - sus!

St. 3.
Thy peace be with us, Je - sus! A - men.

47   In the Cross of Christ I Glory

RATHBUN. 87, 87.

John Bowring, 1792-1872   Ithamar Conkey, 1815-1867

Broadly

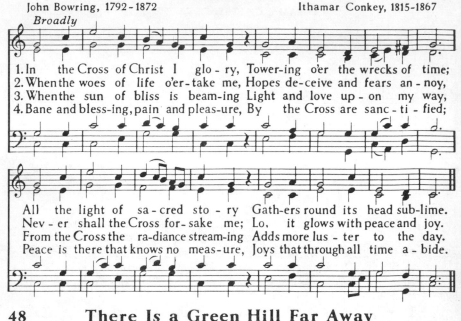

1. In the Cross of Christ I glo - ry, Tower-ing o'er the wrecks of time;
2. When the woes of life o'er-take me, Hopes de-ceive and fears an - noy,
3. When the sun of bliss is beam-ing Light and love up - on my way,
4. Bane and bless-ing, pain and pleas-ure, By the Cross are sanc - ti - fied;

All the light of sa - cred sto - ry Gath-ers round its head sub-lime.
Nev - er shall the Cross for-sake me; Lo, it glows with peace and joy.
From the Cross the ra-diance stream-ing Adds more lus - ter to the day.
Peace is there that knows no meas-ure, Joys that through all time a - bide.

48   There Is a Green Hill Far Away

HORSLEY. C. M.

Cecil F. Alexander, 1823-1895   William Horsley, 1774-1858

In moderate time

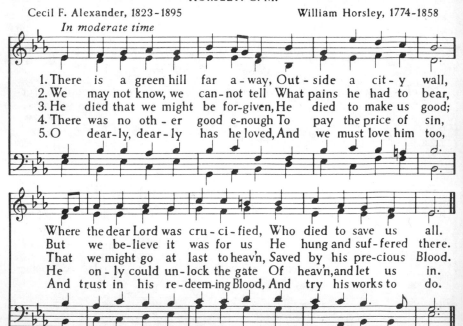

1. There is a green hill far a - way, Out - side a cit - y wall,
2. We may not know, we can-not tell What pains he had to bear,
3. He died that we might be for-given, He died to make us good;
4. There was no oth - er good e-nough To pay the price of sin,
5. O dear-ly, dear - ly has he loved, And we must love him too,

Where the dear Lord was cru - ci - fied, Who died to save us all.
But we be-lieve it was for us He hung and suf-fered there.
That we might go at last to heav'n, Saved by his pre-cious Blood.
He on - ly could un-lock the gate Of heav'n, and let us in.
And trust in his re-deem-ing Blood, And try his works to do.

Beneath the Cross of Jesus 49
ST. CHRISTOPHER. 76, 76. D.

Elizabeth C. Clephane, 1830-1869   Frederick C. Maker, 1844-1927

Devotionally

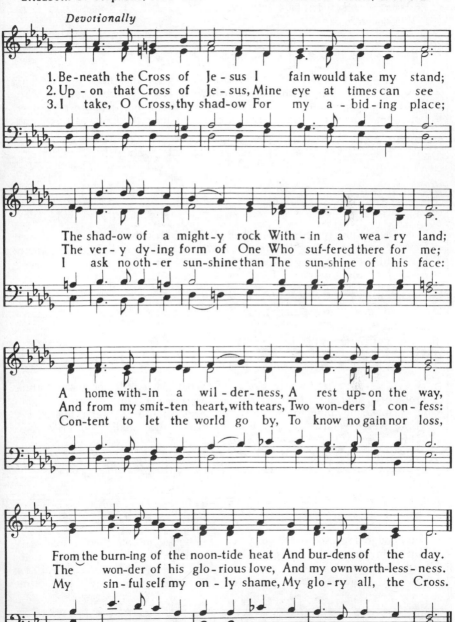

1. Be-neath the Cross of Je-sus I fain would take my stand;
2. Up-on that Cross of Je-sus, Mine eye at times can see
3. I take, O Cross, thy shad-ow For my a-bid-ing place;

The shad-ow of a might-y rock With-in a wea-ry land;
The ver-y dy-ing form of One Who suf-fered there for me;
I ask no oth-er sun-shine than The sun-shine of his face:

A home with-in a wil-der-ness, A rest up-on the way,
And from my smit-ten heart, with tears, Two won-ders I con-fess:
Con-tent to let the world go by, To know no gain nor loss,

From the burn-ing of the noon-tide heat And bur-dens of the day.
The won-der of his glo-rious love, And my own worth-less-ness.
My sin-ful self my on-ly shame, My glo-ry all, the Cross.

50 O Sacred Head

PASSION CHORALE. 76, 76. D.

Ascribed to Bernard of Clairvaux, 1091-1153
Paul Gerhardt, 1607-1676
Tr. James W. Alexander, 1804-1859, alt.

Hans Leo Hassler, 1564-1612
Adapt. and harm.
J. S. Bach, 1685-1750

With devotion

1. O sa-cred Head, now wound-ed, With grief and shame weighed down,
2. How art thou pale with an-guish, With sore a-buse and scorn;
3. What lan-guage shall I bor-row To thank thee, dear-est Friend,
4. Be near when I am dy-ing, O show thy Cross to me!

Now scorn-ful-ly sur-round-ed With thorns, thine on-ly crown;
How does that vis-age lan-guish Which once was bright as morn!
For this thy dy-ing sor-row, Thy pit-y with-out end?
And, for my suc-cor fly-ing, Come, Lord, to set me free.

O sa-cred Head, what glo-ry, What bliss till now was thine!
Thy grief and bit-ter pas-sion Were all for sin-ners' gain;
O make me thine for ev-er, And should I faint-ing be,
These eyes, new faith re-ciev-ing, From thee shall nev-er move;

Yet, though de-spised and go-ry, I joy to call thee mine.
Mine, mine was the trans-gres-sion, But thine the dead-ly pain.
Lord, let me nev-er, nev-er Out-live my love to thee.
For he who dies be-liev-ing Dies safe-ly in thy love. A-men.

Print Thine Image

51

PSALM 42 (FREU DICH SEHR). 87, 87, 77, 88.

Thomas H. Kingo, 1634–1703
Tr. Jens C. Aaberg, 1877–

Genevan Psalter, 1551
Adapt. and harm. J. S. Bach, 1685–1750

Brightly

Print thine im - age, pure and ho - ly, On my heart, O
Lord of Grace; So that noth - ing, high or low - ly,
Thy blest like-ness can ef - face. Let the clear in - scrip-tion be:
Je - sus, cru - ci - fied for me, And the Lord of all cre - a -
tion, Be my ref - uge and sal - va - tion. A - men.

Words from the SERVICE BOOK AND HYMNAL. *Used by permission.*

52 Ah, Holy Jesus

HERZLIEBSTER JESU. 11 11 11, 5.

Johann Heermann, 1585 -1647
Tr. Robert Bridges, 1844-1930

Johann Crüger, 1598-1662

Slowly and solemnly

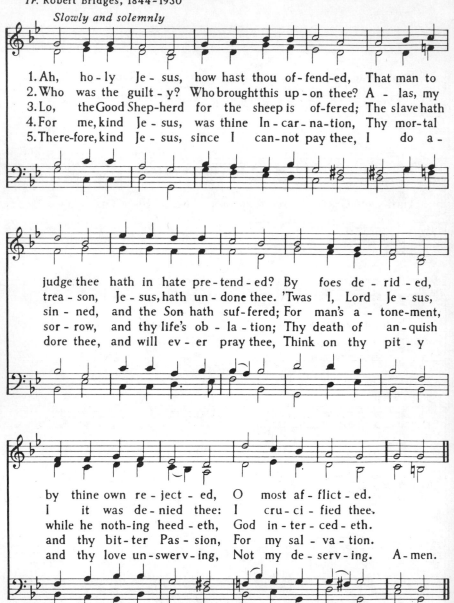

1. Ah, ho-ly Je-sus, how hast thou of-fend-ed, That man to judge thee hath in hate pre-tend-ed? By foes de-rid-ed, by thine own re-ject-ed, O most af-flict-ed.

2. Who was the guilt-y? Who brought this up-on thee? A-las, my trea-son, Je-sus, hath un-done thee. 'Twas I, Lord Je-sus, I it was de-nied thee: I cru-ci-fied thee.

3. Lo, the Good Shep-herd for the sheep is of-fered; The slave hath sin-ned, and the Son hath suf-fered; For man's a-tone-ment, while he noth-ing heed-eth, God in-ter-ced-eth.

4. For me, kind Je-sus, was thine In-car-na-tion, Thy mor-tal sor-row, and thy life's ob-la-tion; Thy death of an-guish and thy bit-ter Pas-sion, For my sal-va-tion.

5. There-fore, kind Je-sus, since I can-not pay thee, I do a-dore thee, and will ev-er pray thee, Think on thy pit-y and thy love un-swerv-ing, Not my de-serv-ing. A-men.

Words from THE YATTENDON HYMNAL, edited by Robert Bridges. By permission of Oxford University Press.

Come to Calvary's Holy Mountain 53

HOLY MOUNTAIN. 87, 87, 77.

James Montgomery, 1771-1854

Ludvig M. Lindeman, 1812-1887

In flowing style

1. Come to Cal-vary's ho-ly moun-tain, Sin-ners, ruined
2. Come in pov-er-ty and mean-ness, Come de-filed, with-
3. Come in sor-row and con-tri-tion, Wound-ed, im-po-
4. He that drinks shall live for ev-er; 'Tis a soul-re-

by the fall; Here a pure and heal-ing foun-tain
out, with-in; From in-fec-tion and un-clean-ness,
tent, and blind; Here the guilt-y, free re-mis-sion,
new-ing flood: God is faith-ful; God will nev-er

Flows to you, to me, to all; In a full per-
From the lep-ro-sy of sin, Wash your robes and
Here the trou-bled, peace may find: Health this foun-tain
Break his cov-e-nant of blood, Signed when our Re-

pet-ual tide, O-pened when our Sav-ior died.
make them white; Ye shall walk with God in light.
will re-store; He that drinks shall thirst no more.
deem-er died, Sealed when he was glo-ri-fied.

54 ## Were You There
WERE YOU THERE. Irregular.

Negro Spiritual   Negro Spiritual

With reverence

1. Were you there when they cru - ci - fied my Lord? Were you
2. Were you there when they nailed him to the tree? Were you
3. Were you there when they laid him in the tomb? Were you
4. Were you there when he rose up from the tomb? Were you

there when they cru - ci - fied my Lord? O, _____
there when they nailed him to the tree? O, _____
there when they laid him in the tomb? O, _____
there when he rose up from the tomb? O, _____

some-times it caus - es me to trem-ble, trem-ble, trem-ble.
some-times it caus - es me to trem-ble, trem-ble, trem-ble.
some-times it caus - es me to trem-ble, trem-ble, trem-ble.
some-times it caus - es me to trem-ble, trem-ble, trem-ble.

Were you there when they cru - ci - fied my Lord?
Were you there when they nailed him to the tree?
Were you there when they laid him in the tomb?
Were you there when he rose up from the tomb?

Wondrous Love

WONDROUS LOVE. 12 9, 12 9.

Traditional

Traditional Southern Folk-Hymn
Harm. Paul Christiansen

Quietly

1. What won-drous love is this, O my soul, O my soul! What
2. What won-drous love is this, O my soul, O my soul! What

won-drous love is this, O my soul! That caused the Lord of Life to
won-drous love is this, O my soul! That Christ should lay a-side his

bear the heav-y Cross, What won-drous love is this, O my soul!
crown for my soul, What won-drous love is this, O my soul!

Harmonization copyright, Augsburg Publishing House.

The Cross and Crown is a rich symbol, full of meaning. It brings to mind several things. It reminds us that our Savior died on the Cross and that he rose again to be our King forever. It also reminds us of God's promise: "Be faithful unto death, and I will give you the crown of life" (Revelation 2:10).

56 When I Survey the Wondrous Cross

HAMBURG. L. M.

Isaac Watts, 1674-1748

Arr. Lowell Mason, 1792-1872

In moderate time

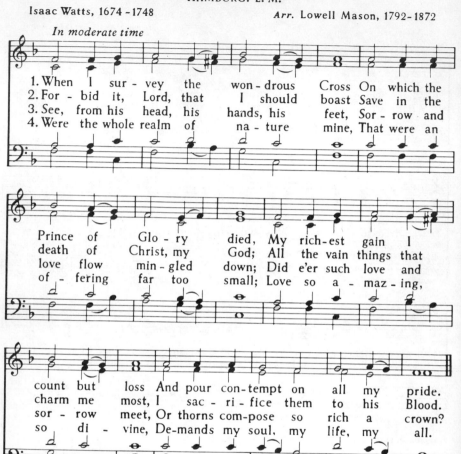

1. When I sur-vey the won-drous Cross On which the
2. For-bid it, Lord, that I should boast Save in the
3. See, from his head, his hands, his feet, Sor-row and
4. Were the whole realm of na-ture mine, That were an

Prince of Glo-ry died, My rich-est gain I
death of Christ, my God; All the vain things that
love flow min-gled down; Did e'er such love and
of-fering far too small; Love so a-maz-ing,

count but loss And pour con-tempt on all my pride.
charm me most, I sac-ri-fice them to his Blood.
sor-row meet, Or thorns com-pose so rich a crown?
so di-vine, De-mands my soul, my life, my all.

How completely God changes things!

When Jesus was crucified, death on a cross was the most cruel and shameful kind of death—the way of death for the worst criminals.

But now the Cross is a symbol of Life. Now the Cross is the shining sign of God's love. Now we sing about the *wondrous* Cross—because Jesus died *for us,* and gave his life for our salvation.

Glory Be to Jesus

57

CASWALL. 65, 65.

Italian, XVIII *cent.*
Tr. Edward Caswall, 1814-1878

Friedrich Filitz, 1804-1876

Slowly and reverently

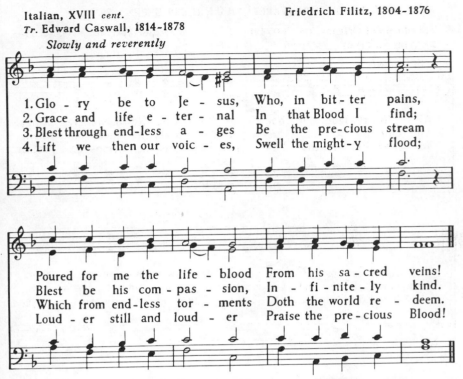

1. Glo - ry be to Je - sus, Who, in bit - ter pains,
2. Grace and life e - ter - nal In that Blood I find;
3. Blest through end-less a - ges Be the pre-cious stream
4. Lift we then our voic - es, Swell the might-y flood;

Poured for me the life - blood From his sa - cred veins!
Blest be his com - pas - sion, In - fi - nite - ly kind.
Which from end-less tor - ments Doth the world re - deem.
Loud - er still and loud - er Praise the pre - cious Blood!

Lent and Holy Week are solemn and serious times. The hymns used during this season remind us of the seriousness of sin, and the seriousness of God in giving his Son to die for us.

At the same time, Lent and Holy Week have the sound of praise and Christian joy. Here in the Gospel of the Cross, God gives us the great good news: "God so loved the world that he gave his only Son" (John 3:16). In this same Gospel, God assures us that for Jesus' sake he freely forgives us and receives us as his children.

Lent and Holy Week then bring us days to sing hymns like *Glory Be to Jesus*. They bring us days for quiet and reverent thought . . . days for thankful, joyful celebration . . . days for singing prayers and praises to our heavenly Father who has bought us with the precious Blood and the redeeming death of his Son, our Savior, Jesus Christ.

58 All Glory, Laud, and Honor

ST. THEODULPH (VALET WILL ICH DIR GEBEN). 76, 76. D.

Theodulph of Orleans, *ctr.* 760-821
Tr. John M. Neale, 1818-1866

Melchior Teschner, 1585-1635

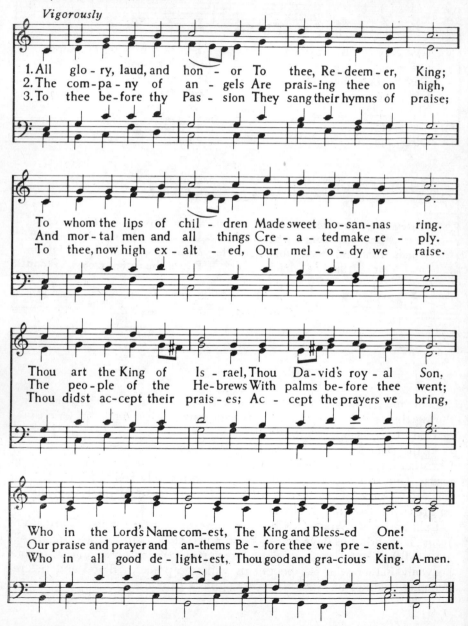

Vigorously

1. All glo - ry, laud, and hon - or To thee, Re - deem - er, King;
2. The com - pa - ny of an - gels Are prais - ing thee on high,
3. To thee be - fore thy Pas - sion They sang their hymns of praise;

To whom the lips of chil - dren Made sweet ho - san - nas ring.
And mor - tal men and all things Cre - a - ted make re - ply.
To thee, now high ex - alt - ed, Our mel - o - dy we raise.

Thou art the King of Is - rael, Thou Da - vid's roy - al Son,
The peo - ple of the He - brews With palms be - fore thee went;
Thou didst ac - cept their prais - es; Ac - cept the prayers we bring,

Who in the Lord's Name com - est, The King and Bless - ed One!
Our praise and prayer and an - thems Be - fore thee we pre - sent.
Who in all good de - light - est,. Thou good and gra - cious King. A - men.

Ride On, Ride On in Majesty

ST. DROSTANE. L. M.

59

Henry H. Milman, 1791-1868, *alt.*

John B. Dykes, 1823-1876

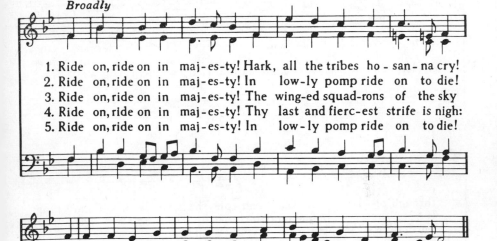

1. Ride on, ride on in maj-es-ty! Hark, all the tribes ho-san-na cry!
2. Ride on, ride on in maj-es-ty! In lowly pomp ride on to die!
3. Ride on, ride on in maj-es-ty! The wing-ed squad-rons of the sky
4. Ride on, ride on in maj-es-ty! Thy last and fierc-est strife is nigh:
5. Ride on, ride on in maj-es-ty! In low-ly pomp ride on to die!

O Sav-ior meek, pur-sue thy road With palms and scattered garments strowed.
O Christ, thy triumphs now be-gin O'er cap-tive death and conquered sin.
Look down with sad and wondering eyes To see the approaching sac-ri-fice.
The Fa-ther on his sapphire throne Ex-pects his own a-noint-ed Son.
Bow thy meek head to mor-tal pain, Then take, O God, thy power and reign.

—No. 59

All Glory, Laud, and Honor.

As you sing the hymn on the opposite page you join the millions who have sung it for over a thousand years—since the time it was written by St. Theodulph, a bishop and poet of the church in the days of Charlemagne.

Each Palm Sunday you also join millions of men, women, and children in all parts of the world, for this is a hymn sung by Christians of nearly all the churches, lands, and languages we know.

God be praised for these vast multitudes with whom we can sing as did the multitudes on the first Palm Sunday: "Hosanna to the Son of David! Blessed be he who comes in the name of the Lord! Hosanna in the highest!" (Matthew 21:9).

60 Hosanna, Loud Hosanna

ELLACOMBE. C. M. D.

Jennette Threlfall, 1821-1880   Württemberg *Gesangbuch,* 1784

With spirit

1. Ho - san - na, loud ho - san - na, The lit - tle chil - dren sang;
2. From Ol - i - vet they fol - lowed 'Mid an ex - ul - tant crowd,
3. 'Ho - san - na in the high - est!' That an - cient song we sing,

Through pil - lared court and tem - ple The love - ly an - them rang;
The vic - tor palm-branch wav - ing, And chant-ing clear and loud;
For Christ is our Re - deem - er, The Lord of heaven, our King.

To Je - sus, who had blessed them Close fold - ed to his breast,
The Lord of men and an - gels Rode on in low - ly state,
O may we ev - er praise him With heart and life and voice,

The chil - dren sang their prais - es, The sim - plest and the best.
Nor scorned that lit - tle chil - dren Should on his bid - ding wait.
And in his bliss - ful pres - ence E - ter - nal - ly re - joice. A - men.

EASTER
Jesus Christ Is Risen Today

61

EASTER HYMN (WORGAN). 77, 77. With Alleluias.

Latin, XIV *cent.*
Tr. *Lyra Davidica,* 1708
St. 4, Charles Wesley, 1707-1788

Lyra Davidica, 1708

With dignity

1. Jesus Christ is risen to-day, Al - le - lu - ia!
2. Hymns of praise then let us sing, Al - le - lu - ia!
3. But the pains which he en-dured, Al - le - lu - ia!
4. Sing we to our God a-bove, Al - le - lu - ia!

Our tri-um-phant ho-ly day, Al - le - lu - ia!
Un-to Christ, our heaven-ly King, Al - le - lu - ia!
Our sal-va-tion have pro-cured; Al - le - lu - ia!
Praise e-ter-nal as his love; Al - le - lu - ia!

Who did once, up-on the Cross, Al - le - lu - ia!
Who en-dured the Cross and grave, Al - le - lu - ia!
Now a-bove the sky he's King, Al - le - lu - ia!
Praise him, all ye heaven-ly host, Al - le - lu - ia!

Suf-fer to re-deem our loss. Al - le - lu - ia!
Sin-ners to re-deem and save. Al - le - lu - ia!
Where the an-gels ev-er sing. Al - le - lu - ia!
Fa-ther, Son, and Ho-ly Ghost. Al - le - lu - ia!

62 Christ, the Lord, Is Risen Today

LLANFAIR. 77, 77. With Alleluias.

Latin Sequence, *Victimae Paschali*
Tr. Jane E. Leeson, 1807-1882

Robert Williams, *cir.* 1781-1821

Broadly, with dignity

1. Christ, the Lord, is risen to-day; Al - le - lu - ia!
2. For the sheep the Lamb hath bled, Al - le - lu - ia!
3. Christ, the Vic-tim un - de - filed, Al - le - lu - ia!
4. Chris-tians, on this hap-py day, Al - le - lu - ia!

Chris-tians, haste your vows to pay; Al - le - lu - ia!
Sin - less in the sin - ner's stead; Al - le - lu - ia!
God and man hath rec - on - ciled; Al - le - lu - ia!
Haste with joy your vows to pay; Al - le - lu - ia!

Of - fer ye your prais - es meet, Al - le - lu - ia!
Christ is risen, to - day we cry; Al - le - lu - ia!
Whilst in strange and aw - ful strife, Al - le - lu - ia!
Christ is risen, to - day we cry; Al - le - lu - ia!

At the Pas - chal Vic - tim's feet. Al - le - lu - ia!
Now he lives no more to. die. Al - le - lu - ia!
Met to - geth - er death and life. Al - le - lu - ia!
Now he lives no more to die. Al - le - lu - ia!

5. Christ who once for sinners bled, Alleluia!
Now the first-born from the dead, Alleluia!
Throned in endless might and power, Alleluia!
Lives and reigns for evermore. Alleluia!

6. Hail, Eternal Hope on high! Alleluia!
Hail, thou King of Victory! Alleluia!
Hail, thou Prince of Life adored! Alleluia!
Help and save us, gracious Lord. Alleluia!

Alleluia! Jesus Lives 63

EASTER GLORY (FRED TIL BOD). 77, 77, 77.

Carl B. Garve, 1763-1841
Tr. Laurence N. Field, 1896-

Ludvig M. Lindeman, 1812-1887

Triumphantly

1. Al-le-lu-ia! Je - sus lives! Won the bat-tle glo-ri-ous!
2. Al-le-lu-ia! O my soul, Life e-ter-nal waits for thee;
3. Al-le-lu-ia! Heaven-ly choirs Joy-ful-ly their voic-es raise!

From the gloom-y vault of death He hath come vic-to-ri-ous,
Saved by him, the Liv-ing One, Where he is, thou too shalt be,
Let us mor-tals here be-low Blend with theirs our songs of praise.

Lead-ing to their heaven-ly home Count-less mul-ti-tudes to come.
Safe with-in the prom-ised land, With the Lord at God's right hand.
Glo-ry to the e-ter-nal Son! Glo-ry to the Ris-en One!

64   Come, Ye Faithful, Raise the Strain

SPRING OF SOULS. 76, 76. D. Trochaic.

John of Damascus, VIII *cent.*
Tr. John M. Neale, 1818-1866, *alt.*

Ludvig M. Lindeman, 1812-1887

Triumphantly

1. Come, ye faith - ful, raise the strain Of tri - um - phant glad - ness;
2. Now the queen of sea-sons, bright With the day of splen - dor,
3. All the win - ter of our sins, Long and dark, is fly - ing
4. But to-day a-midst the Twelve Thou didst stand, be - stow - ing

God hath brought his Is - ra - el In - to joy from sad - ness;
With the roy - al feast of feasts, Comes its joy to ren - der;
From his light, to whom we give Laud and praise un - dy - ing.
That thy peace, which ev - er-more Pass - eth hu - man know - ing.

'Tis the spring of souls to - day: Christ hath burst his pris - on,
Comes to glad-den Chris-tian men, Who with true af - fec - tion
Nei - ther might the gates of death, Nor the tomb's dark por - tal,
Come, ye faith-ful, raise the strain Of tri - um-phant glad-ness;

And from three days' sleep in death, As a sun hath ris - en,
Wel-come in un - wea-ried strains Je - sus' res-ur - rec-tion.
Nor the watch-ers, nor the seal, Hold thee as a mor-tal.
God hath brought his Is - ra - el In - to joy from sad-ness.

Good Christian Men, Rejoice and Sing   65

VULPIUS (GELOBT SEI GOTT). 888. With Alleluias.

Cyril A. Alington, 1872-1955

Melchior Vulpius, *ctr.* 1560

Harm. Ernest MacMillan, 1893-

With exultation

1. Good Chris-tian men, re - joice and sing! Now is the
2. The Lord of Life is risen for aye; Bring flowers of
3. Praise we in songs of vic - to - ry That love, that
4. Thy Name we bless, O ris - en Lord, And sing to -

tri - umph of our King! To all the world glad news we bring:
song to strew his way; Let all man-kind re-joice and say:
life which can - not die! And sing with hearts up-lift-ed high:
day with one ac-cord The life laid down, the life re - stored:

Al - le - lu - ia! Al - le - lu - ia! Al-le-lu - ia!
Al - le - lu - ia! Al - le - lu - ia! Al-le-lu - ia!
Al - le - lu - ia! Al - le - lu - ia! Al-le-lu - ia!
Al - le - lu - ia! Al - le - lu - ia! Al-le-lu - ia!

66 The World Itself Keeps Easter Day

87, 87, 88, 87.

John M. Neale, 1818-1866, *alt.*

Plae Cantiones, 1582
Harm. Marie Pooler, 1928-

Joyfully

1. The world it-self keeps East-er Day, And East-er larks are sing - ing;
2. There stood three Mar-ys by the tomb, On East-er morn-ing ear - ly;
3. But ear - lier still the an-gel sped, His news of com-fort giv - ing:

And East-er flow'rs are bloom-ing gay, And East-er buds are spring-ing:
When day had scarce-ly chased the gloom, And dew was white and pearl - y:
And 'Why,' he said, 'a-mong the dead Thus seek ye for the liv - ing?'

Al - le - lu - ia, al - le - lu - ia: The Lord of all things lives a - new,
Al - le - lu - ia, al - le - lu - ia: With lov - ing but with err - ing mind,
Al - le - lu - ia, al - le - lu - ia: The Lord hath risen, as all things tell:

And all his works are ris - ing too: Ho - san - na in ex - cel - sis.
They came the Prince of Life to find: Ho - san - na in ex - cel - sis.
Good Chris-tians, see ye rise as well! Ho - san - na in ex - cel - sis.

Harmonization copyright Augsburg Publishing House.

He Is Risen

NEANDER (UNSER HERRSCHER). 87, 87, 77.

Cecil F. Alexander, 1823-1895, *alt.*   Joachim Neander, 1650-1680

With dignity

1. He is ris-en! He is ris-en! Tell it with a
2. Tell it to the sin-ners, weep-ing O-ver deeds in
3. Come, with high and ho-ly glad-ness, Chant our Lord's tri-
4. He is ris-en! He is ris-en! He has o-pened

joy-ful voice; He has burst his three days' pris-on;
dark-ness done. Wea-ry watch of sor-row keep-ing,
um-phant lay; Not one touch of twi-light sad-ness
heav-en's gate; We are free from sin's dark pris-on,

Let the whole wide earth re-joice: Death is con-quered,
Bright-ly breaks their East-er sun; Blood can wash all
Dims his res-ur-rec-tion day; Bright-ly dawns the
Ris-en to a ho-lier state; Soon a bright-er

man is free, Christ has won the vic-to-ry.
sins a-way, Christ has con-quered hell to-day.
ra-diant east, Bright-er far our East-er Feast.
East-er beam On our long-ing eyes shall stream.

68 That Easter Day with Joy Was Bright

PUER NOBIS NASCITUR. L. M.

Latin hymn, IV or V *cent.*
Tr. John M. Neale, 1818-1866, *alt.*

Composed or adapted by
Michael Praetorius, 1571-1621
Harm. Martin Shaw, 1875-1958

Moderately fast

1. That East-er Day with joy was bright, The sun shone out with fair-er light, When, to their long-ing eyes re-stored, The A-pos-tles saw their ris-en Lord.

2. O Je-sus, King of gen-tle-ness, Do thou our in-most hearts pos-sess; And we to thee will ev-er raise The trib-ute of our grate-ful praise.

3. Je-sus, who art the Lord of all, In this our East-er fes-ti-val, From ev-ery weap-on death can wield, Thine own re-deemed,thy peo-ple, shield!

4. All praise O ris-en Lord, we give To thee, who dead, a-gain dost live; To God the Fa-ther e-qual praise, And God the Ho-ly Ghost, we raise. A-men.

Music reprinted from SONGS OF PRAISE, ENLARGED EDITION, *by permission of* Oxford University Press, London.

Alleluia! Alleluia! Alleluia!

This is our great song at Easter . . . our song in every Easter hymn . . . our song for every day of our lives.

Alleluia means "Praise to God." This is our song of songs . . . for Christ is risen! He is risen indeed!

Now to each one he gives this glorious Gospel: "Because I live, you will live also" (John 14:19).

Alleluia! Alleluia! Alleluia!

The Strife Is O'er

VICTORY. 888. With Alleluias.

Latin, XVII cent.
Tr. Francis Pott, 1832-1909

Palestrina, 1525-1594
Adapt. William H. Monk, 1823-1889
Alleluias by William H. Monk

Broadly, with dignity

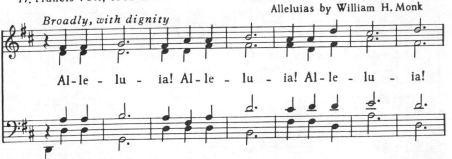

Al-le - lu - ia! Al-le - lu - ia! Al-le - lu - ia!

1. The strife is o'er, the bat - tle done; Now is the Vic - tor's
2. The powers of death have done their worst, But Christ their le - gions
3. The three sad days have quick-ly sped, He ris - es glo - rious
4. He brake the age-bound chains of hell, The bars from heaven's high
5. Lord, by the stripes which wound-ed thee, From death's dread sting thy

tri - umph won; Now be the song of praise be - gun, Al-le - lu - ia!
hath dis-persed; Let shouts of ho - ly joy out - burst, Al-le - lu - ia!
from the dead; All glo - ry to our ris - en Head! Al-le - lu - ia!
por - tals fell; Let hymns of praise his tri - umph tell. Al-le - lu - ia!
serv - ants free, That we may live and sing to thee, Al-le - lu - ia!

ASCENSION

70

Golden Harps Are Sounding

HERMAS. 65, 65. D. With Refrain.

Frances R. Havergal, 1836-1879   Frances R. Havergal, 1836-1879

1. Gold-en harps are sound-ing, An-gel voic-es ring, Pearl-y
gates are o-pened, O-pened for the King. Christ, the King of
Glo-ry, Je-sus, King of Love, Is gone up in tri-umph
To his throne a-bove. 'All his work is end-ed,' Joy-ful-ly we
sing, 'Je-sus hath as-cend-ed, Glo-ry to our King.'

2. He who came to save us, He who bled and died, Now is
crowned with glo-ry At his Fa-ther's side. Nev-er more to
suf-fer, Nev-er more to die, Je-sus, King of Glo-ry,
Has gone up on high.

3. Pray-ing for his chil-dren In that bless-ed place, Call-ing
them to glo-ry, Send-ing them his grace; His bright home pre-
par-ing, Faith-ful ones, for you, Je-sus, ev-er liv-eth,
Ev-er lov-eth, too.

Hail the Day That Sees Him Rise

ASCENSION. 77, 77. With Alleluias.

Charles Wesley, 1707-1788, *alt.*　　　　　　William H. Monk, 1823-1889

Triumphantly

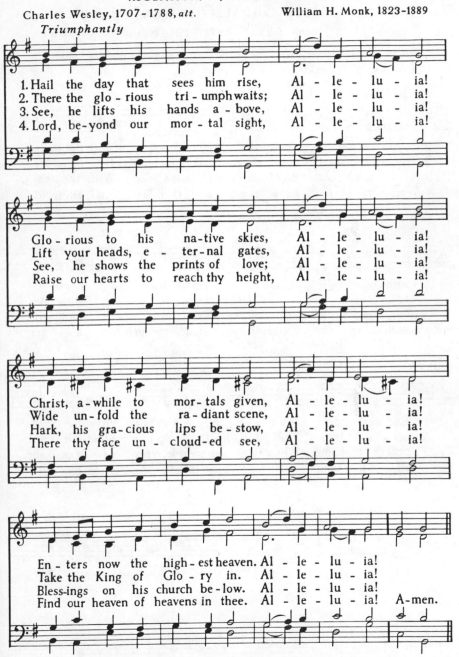

1. Hail the day that sees him rise, Al - le - lu - ia!
2. There the glo - rious tri - umph waits; Al - le - lu - ia!
3. See, he lifts his hands a - bove, Al - le - lu - ia!
4. Lord, be - yond our mor - tal sight, Al - le - lu - ia!

Glo - rious to his na - tive skies, Al - le - lu - ia!
Lift your heads, e - ter - nal gates, Al - le - lu - ia!
See, he shows the prints of love; Al - le - lu - ia!
Raise our hearts to reach thy height, Al - le - lu - ia!

Christ, a - while to mor - tals given, Al - le - lu - ia!
Wide un - fold the ra - diant scene, Al - le - lu - ia!
Hark, his gra - cious lips be - stow, Al - le - lu - ia!
There thy face un - cloud - ed see, Al - le - lu - ia!

En - ters now the high - est heaven. Al - le - lu - ia!
Take the King of Glo - ry in. Al - le - lu - ia!
Bless - ings on his church be - low. Al - le - lu - ia!
Find our heaven of heavens in thee. Al - le - lu - ia! A - men.

This hymn may also be sung to LLANFAIR *(No. 62).*

72 Come, Holy Ghost, Our Souls Inspire

VENI, CREATOR SPIRITUS. L.M.

Based on *Veni, Creator Spiritus*
Tr. John Cosin, 1594-1672

Plainsong Melody, Mode VIII

Broadly

1. Come, Ho - ly Ghost, our souls in - spire And light - en
2. Thy bless - ed unc - tion from a - bove Is com - fort,
3. A - noint and cheer our soil - ed face With the a -
4. Teach us to know the Fa - ther, Son, And thee, of

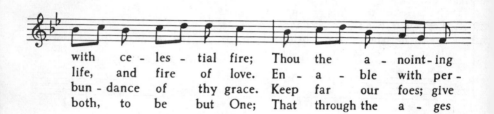

with ce - les - tial fire; Thou the a - noint - ing
life, and fire of love. En - a - ble with per -
bun - dance of thy grace. Keep far our foes; give
both, to be but One; That through the a - ges

Spir - it art Who dost thy seven - fold gifts im - part.
pet - ual light The dull - ness of our blind - ed sight.
peace at home; Where thou art guide, no ill can come.
all a - long This may be our end - less song!

After the last stanza only

Praise to thy e - ter - nal mer - it,

Fa - ther, Son, and Ho - ly Spir - it. A - men.

Come, Holy Spirit, God and Lord

KOMM HEILIGER GEIST, HERRE GOTT. L.M.D. With Alleluias.

Martin Luther, 1483-1546
Tr. Edward T. Horn III, 1909-

Pre-Reformation Melody
Erfurt Gesangbuch, 1524

With dignity

1. Come, Ho - ly Spir- it, God and Lord; Be all thy gifts in plen-ty
2. O strong De-fence, O ho - ly Light! That we may know our God a-
3. O sa- cred Ar - dor, Com-fort sweet! Make will-ing hearts and read-y

poured To save, to strength-en and make whole Each read - y
right, And call him Fa - ther from the heart, The word of
feet That, come what may, in storm and test We an - swer

mind, each wait-ing soul. O by the bright-ness of thy light In
life and truth im - part. Make us to trust in God a - lone, And
on - ly thy be - hest. O quick-en us with all thy powers, Make

ho - ly faith all men u - nite, And to thy praise, by ev - ery tongue,
Je - sus for our Mas-ter own, His yoke and teach-ing ne'er to change
strong our faith in weak-er hours, That, as good Chris-tians in the strife,

In ev-ery land, our hymn be sung. Al-le - lu - ia! Al-le-lu - ia!
For oth-er doc-trines new and strange. Al-le - lu - ia! Al-le-lu - ia!
We turn to thee in death and life. Al-le - lu - ia! Al-le-lu - ia!

Words from the SERVICE BOOK AND HYMNAL. *Used by permission.*

74 O Holy Spirit, Enter In

WIE SCHÖN LEUCHTET. Irregular.

Michael Schirmer, 1606-1673
Philipp Nicolai, 1556-1608
Tr. Catherine Winkworth, 1829-1878
Adapt. and harm. J. S. Bach, 1685-1750

With movement

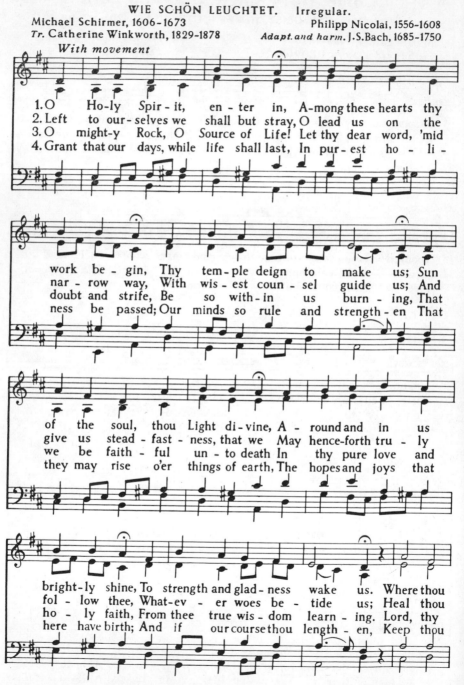

1. O Ho-ly Spir-it, en-ter in, A-mong these hearts thy
2. Left to our-selves we shall but stray, O lead us on the
3. O might-y Rock, O Source of Life! Let thy dear word, 'mid
4. Grant that our days, while life shall last, In pur-est ho-li-

work be-gin, Thy tem-ple deign to make us; Sun
nar-row way, With wis-est coun-sel guide us; And
doubt and strife, Be so with-in us burn-ing, That
ness be passed; Our minds so rule and strength-en That

of the soul, thou Light di-vine, A-round and in us
give us stead-fast-ness, that we May hence-forth tru-ly
we be faith-ful un-to death In thy pure love and
they may rise o'er things of earth, The hopes and joys that

bright-ly shine, To strength and glad-ness wake us. Where thou
fol-low thee, What-ev-er woes be-tide us; Heal thou
ho-ly faith, From thee true wis-dom learn-ing. Lord, thy
here have birth; And if our course thou length-en, Keep thou

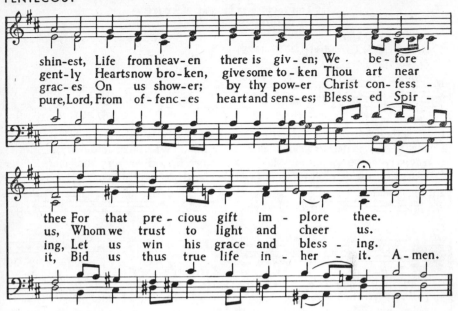

shin-est, Life from heav-en there is giv-en; We be-fore
gent-ly Hearts now bro-ken, give some to-ken Thou art near
grac-es On us show-er; by thy pow-er Christ con-fess -
pure, Lord, From of-fenc-es heart and sens-es; Bless - ed Spir -

thee For that pre-cious gift im-plore thee.
us, Whom we trust to light and cheer us.
ing, Let us win his grace and bless-ing.
it, Bid us thus true life in-her-it. A-men.

Breathe on Me, Breath of God 75
TRENTHAM. S. M.
Edwin Hatch, 1835-1889   Robert Jackson, 1840-1914

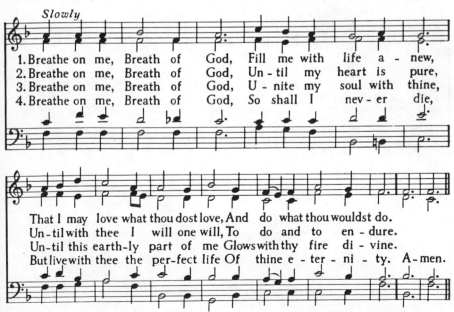

Slowly

1. Breathe on me, Breath of God, Fill me with life a - new,
2. Breathe on me, Breath of God, Un - til my heart is pure,
3. Breathe on me, Breath of God, U - nite my soul with thine,
4. Breathe on me, Breath of God, So shall I nev - er die,

That I may love what thou dost love, And do what thou wouldst do.
Un-til with thee I will one will, To do and to en - dure.
Un-til this earth-ly part of me Glows with thy fire di - vine.
But live with thee the per-fect life Of thine e - ter - ni - ty. A-men.

Music used by permission of Mrs. Ethel Taylor.

76   O Day Full of Grace

WEYSE. 98, 98, 98.

Danish, XIV *cent.*
Nikolai F.S. Grundtvig, 1783-1872
Tr. Composite

Christoph E.F. Weyse, 1774-1842

With dignity

1. O day full of grace, which we be-hold, Now gent-ly to view as-cend-ing; Thou o-ver the earth thy reign un-fold, Good cheer to all mor-tals lend-ing, That chil-dren of light in ev-ery clime May prove that the night is end-ing.

2. How blest was that gra-cious mid-night hour When God in our flesh was giv-en; Then dawn came o'er earth with light and power That spread through the dark-ened heav-en; Then rose o'er the world that Sun di-vine Which gloom from our hearts hath driv-en.

3. Yea, were ev-ery tree en-dowed with speech, And ev-ery small leaf-let sing-ing, They nev-er with praise his worth could reach, Though earth with their praise were ring-ing. Who ful-ly could praise the Light of Life Who light to our souls is bring-ing?

4. With joy we de-part for our fa-ther-land, Where God our Fa-ther is dwell-ing, Where read-y for us his man-sions stand, Where heav-en with praise is swell-ing; And there we shall walk in end-less light, With blest ones his praise forth-tell-ing.

TRINITY

Holy, Holy, Holy

NICAEA. Irregular.

Reginald Heber, 1783-1826

John B. Dykes, 1823-1876

Joyfully, with dignity

1. Ho-ly, ho-ly, ho - ly, Lord God Al - might - y!
2. Ho-ly, ho-ly, ho - ly, all the saints a - dore thee,
3. Ho-ly, ho-ly, ho - ly, though the dark - ness hide thee,
4. Ho-ly, ho-ly, ho - ly, Lord God Al - might - y!

Ear - ly in the morn - ing our song shall rise to thee;
Cast - ing down their gold-en crowns a - round the glass-y sea,
Though the eye of sin - ful man thy glo - ry may not see,
All thy works shall praise thy Name, in earth and sky and sea;

Ho - ly, ho - ly, ho - ly, mer - ci - ful and might - y,
Cher - u - bim and sera - phim fall - ing down be - fore thee,
On - ly thou art ho - ly; there is none be - side thee,
Ho - ly, ho - ly, ho - ly, mer - ci - ful and might - y,

God in three Per - sons, bless-ed Trin - i - ty!
Which wert, and art, and ev - er - more shalt be.
Per - fect in power, in love, and pu - ri - ty.
God in three Per - sons, bless-ed Trin - i - ty! A-men.

78 Glory to the Father Give

INNOCENTS. 77, 77.

Author unknown

The Parish Choir, London, 1850

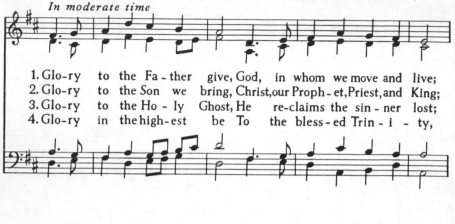

In moderate time

1. Glo-ry to the Fa - ther give, God, in whom we move and live;
2. Glo-ry to the Son we bring, Christ, our Proph-et, Priest, and King;
3. Glo-ry to the Ho - ly Ghost, He re-claims the sin - ner lost;
4. Glo-ry in the high-est be To the bless-ed Trin - i - ty,

Chil-dren's prayers he deigns to hear, Chil-dren's songs de-light his ear.
Chil-dren raise your sweet-est strain To the Lamb, for he was slain.
Chil-dren's minds may he in-spire, Touch their tongues with ho-ly fire.
For the Gos - pel from a - bove, For the word that 'God is love.'

There are many symbols for the Holy Trinity. The best ones try to show that there are three persons: the Father, the Son, and the Holy Spirit. Yet these three persons are one God who cannot be separated. The Holy Trinity is a mystery which we cannot fully understand.

Blessed Father, Great Creator

REGENT SQUARE. 87, 87, 87.

John Cawood, 1775-1852   Henry Smart, 1813-1879

Moderate, with dignity

1. Bless-ed Fa-ther, great Cre-a-tor! Hum-bly at thy feet we bend;
2. Bless-ed Je-sus, great Re-deem-er! Sad-ly by thy Cross we stand;
3. Bless-ed Spir-it, great Con-sol-er! Make our hearts thy dwell-ing place;
4. Bless-ed Fa-ther, Son, and Spir-it, Glo-rious God-head, Three in One!

To thy throne for all thy fa-vors, Youth-ful prais-es now we send.
On that Cross thou diedst to bring us To the joys of thy right hand.
Teach us, guide us, sanc-ti-fy us, And con-sole us all our days.
Guide us to the heaven of heav-ens, Through the mer-its of the Son.

Bless-ed Fa-ther! Bless-ed Fa-ther! To our youth-ful songs at-tend.
Bless-ed Je-sus! Bless-ed Je-sus! Bring us to thy heaven-ly land.
Bless-ed Spir-it! Bless-ed Spir-it! Ev-er cheer us with thy grace.
Guide and guard us, guide and guard us, Till we see him on the throne. A-men.

Blessed be the Holy Trinity, and the undivided Unity.
Let us give glory to him because he hath shown
     his mercy to us.
O Lord our Lord, how excellent is thy Name in all
     the earth!

—Introit for the Festival
of the Holy Trinity

80 Father Most Holy, Merciful and Tender

CHRISTE SANCTORUM. 11 11 11,5.

Latin Hymn, *ctr.* X *cent.*
Tr. Percy Dearmer, 1867-1936

XVIII *cent.* French Church Melody
Harm. Ralph Vaughan Williams, 1872-1958

In moderate time

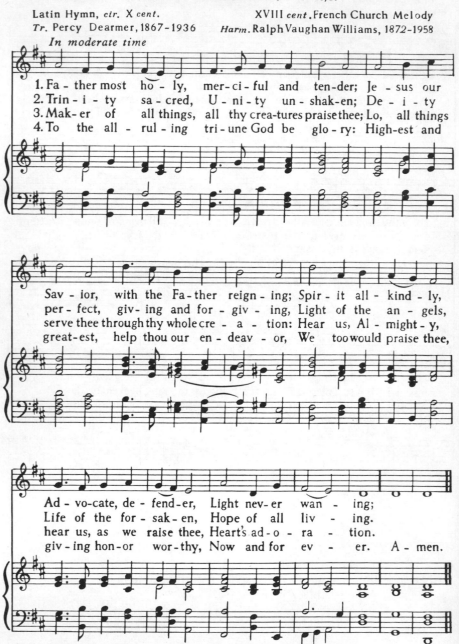

1. Fa - ther most ho - ly, mer - ci - ful and ten-der; Je - sus our
2. Trin - i - ty sa - cred, U - ni - ty un - shak-en; De - i - ty
3. Mak- er of all things, all thy crea-tures praise thee; Lo, all things
4. To the all - rul - ing tri - une God be glo - ry: High-est and

Sav - ior, with the Fa - ther reign - ing; Spir - it all - kind - ly,
per - fect, giv - ing and for - giv - ing, Light of the an - gels,
serve thee through thy whole cre - a - tion: Hear us, Al - might - y,
great-est, help thou our en - deav - or, We too would praise thee,

Ad - vo-cate, de - fend-er, Light nev-er wan - ing;
Life of the for - sak - en, Hope of all liv - ing.
hear us, as we raise thee, Heart's ad - o - ra - tion.
giv-ing hon-or wor-thy, Now and for ev - er. A - men.

Text and harmony from THE ENGLISH HYMNAL *by permission of Oxford University Press.*

All Glory Be to God on High

ALLEIN GOTT IN DER HÖH. 87, 87, 887.

Ascribed to Nikolaus Decius, *d.* 1541
Nikolaus Decius, *d.* 1541
Tr. Catherine Winkworth, 1829-1878, *alt.*

Joyfully, with breadth

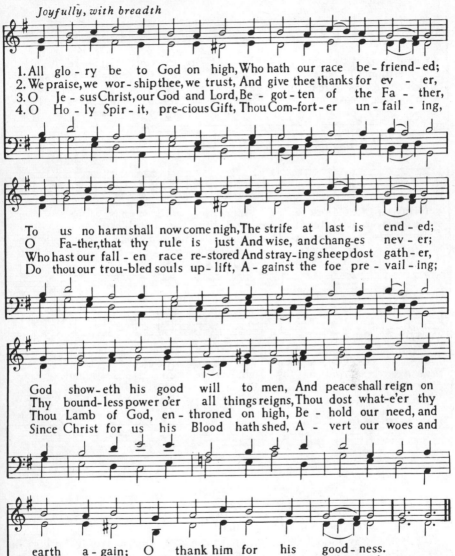

1. All glo-ry be to God on high, Who hath our race be-friend-ed;
2. We praise, we wor-ship thee, we trust, And give thee thanks for ev - er,
3. O Je-sus Christ, our God and Lord, Be-got-ten of the Fa - ther,
4. O Ho-ly Spir-it, pre-cious Gift, Thou Com-fort-er un-fail-ing,

To us no harm shall now come nigh, The strife at last is end-ed;
O Fa-ther, that thy rule is just And wise, and chang-es nev-er;
Who hast our fall-en race re-stored And stray-ing sheep dost gath-er,
Do thou our trou-bled souls up-lift, A-gainst the foe pre-vail-ing;

God show-eth his good will to men, And peace shall reign on
Thy bound-less power o'er all things reigns, Thou dost what-e'er thy
Thou Lamb of God, en-throned on high, Be-hold our need, and
Since Christ for us his Blood hath shed, A-vert our woes and

earth a-gain; O thank him for his good-ness.
will or-dains: 'Tis well thou art our Rul-er!
hear our cry: Have mer-cy on us, Je-sus!
calm our dread; We trust in thee to help us! A-men.

Come, Thou Almighty King

MOSCOW (ITALIAN HYMN). 664, 6664.

Authorship uncertain
Whitefield's Collection, 1757, alt.

Felice de Giardini, 1716-1796

Joyfully

1. Come, thou al-might-y King, Help us thy Name to sing, Help us to praise! Fa-ther all glo-ri-ous, O'er all vic-to-ri-ous, Come and reign o-ver us; An-cient of Days.

2. Come, thou In-car-nate Word, Gird on thy might-y sword; Our prayer at-tend; Come and thy peo-ple bless, And give thy word suc-cess, And let thy right-eous-ness To us de-scend.

3. Come, Ho-ly Com-fort-er, Thy sa-cred wit-ness bear In this glad hour: Thou who al-might-y art, Now rule in ev-ery heart, And ne'er from us de-part, Spir-it of power.

4. To thee, great One in Three, E-ter-nal prais-es be, Hence, ev-er-more! Thy sov-ereign maj-es-ty May we in glo-ry see, And to e-ter-ni-ty Love and a-dore. A-men.

God the Father, Son, and Holy Spirit.

This is the way God tells us about himself. As our heavenly Father, he sends and gives us his Son, our Lord Jesus Christ. In our Lord Jesus Christ he gives his own life to redeem us. Then through the work of the Holy Spirit he gives us grace and power to believe in Christ our Savior.

So we confess our Triune God. So we pray to Father, Son, and Holy Spirit. And so we live . . . to praise him who is the Lord of our life and the God of our salvation.

O Father, Son, and Holy Spirit

COKE-JEPHCOTT. 10 10, 10 10.

James Boeringer, 1930-   James Boeringer, 1930-

Devotionally

1. O   Fa - ther,   Son,   and   Ho - ly Spir - it, hear;
2. Should faith   in   Christ's re - demp-tion fall a - way;
3. Our   Fa - ther,   from pride's bond-age set us   free,
4. Dear   Son   of   God,   who   in Geth-sem-a - ne
5. O   Ho - ly   Spir - it,   grace be - stow that we

Thou   who   dost   know   our   doubt-ing and our grief,
And   fear   de - vour,   and   doubt come like a thief,
Since   an - y   man   of   sin - ners might be chief;
Didst   bear   our   bur - dens,   find - ing no re - lief;
May   grow   in   faith, though years of life be brief;

Grant   the   pe - ti - tion   of each heart sin - cere:
To   steal   our   peace   and   joy, help each to pray:
Hum - ble   our   souls   that each may cry to thee:
De - stroy   temp - ta - tion's power and hear each plea:
Till   faith   shall   lead   to   sight, our prayer shall be:

'Lord,   I   be - lieve; help thou mine un-be - lief.'
'Lord,   I   be - lieve; help thou mine un-be - lief.'
'Lord,   I   be - lieve; help thou mine un-be - lief.'
'Lord,   I   be - lieve; help thou mine un-be - lief.'
'Lord,   I   be - lieve; help thou mine un-be - lief.' A - men.

The Church

COMMUNION OF SAINTS

The Church's One Foundation

AURELIA. 76, 76. D.

Samuel J. Stone, 1839 - 1900

Samuel S. Wesley, 1810 - 1876

With breadth and dignity

1. The church's one foun - da - tion Is Je - sus Christ her Lord;
2. E - lect from ev - ery na - tion, Yet one o'er all the earth,
3. 'Mid toil and trib - u - la - tion, And tu - mult of her war,
4. Yet she on earth hath un - ion With God, the Three in One,

She is his new cre - a - tion By wa - ter and the word:
Her char - ter of sal - va - tion One Lord, one faith, one birth;
She waits the con - sum - ma - tion Of peace for ev - er - more;
And mys - tic sweet com - mun - ion With those whose rest is won.

From heaven he came and sought her To be his ho - ly bride,
One ho - ly Name she bless - es, Par - takes one ho - ly food,
Till with the vi - sion glo - rious Her long - ing eyes are blest,
O hap - py ones and ho - ly! Lord, give us grace that we

With his own Blood he bought her, And for her life he died.
And to one hope she press - es, With ev - ery grace en - dued.
And the great church vic - to - rious Shall be the church at rest.
Like them, the meek and low - ly, On high may dwell with thee. A - men.

Lord, Keep Us Steadfast in Thy Word 85

ERHALT UNS, HERR. L. M.

Martin Luther, 1483-1546
Tr. Catherine Winkworth, 1829-1878

Martin Luther, 1483-1546
Based on Plainsong Melody, Mode II,
Jesu, dulcedo cordium

Devotionally

1. Lord, keep us stead-fast in thy word, Curb
2. Lord Je-sus Christ, thy power make known, For
3. O Com-fort-er of price-less worth, Send

those who fain by craft or sword Would wrest the king-dom from thy
thou art Lord of Lords a-lone; De-fend thy Chris-ten-dom, that
peace and u-ni-ty on earth; Sup-port us in our fi-nal

Son, And set at naught all he hath done.
we May ev-er-more sing praise to thee.
strife, And lead us out of death to life. A-men.

Lord, Keep Us Steadfast in Thy Word is Martin Luther's great hymn of prayer for the Holy Christian Church.

As you sing its short, strong stanzas, sing them with fervent prayer for yourself and for all your fellow Christians . . . for those you know . . . and for the unnumbered millions you do not know.

When you sing each stanza, pray as you can imagine Luther prayed these lines . . . with strong and steadfast faith in God the Father, Son, and Holy Spirit.

86 Behold a Host

BEHOLD A HOST. 88, 86. 12 Lines.

Hans A. Brorson, 1694-1764
English Version from
Service Book and Hymnal, 1955

Norwegian Folksong
Arr. Edvard Grieg, 1843-1907

Flowing

1. Be - hold a host like moun - tains bright! Lo, who are
2. Then sing, ye con - quering le - gions white, Let myr - iad

these, ar - rayed in white, A glo - rious band, with
voic - es hail his might, And praise the Lord, who

palms in hand A - round the throne of light? Lo, these are
by his word Hath stab - lished you in light. Ye, who all

they who o - ver - came Great trib - u - la - tion
earth-ly lure did flee, Who sowed and toiled, but

Words from the SERVICE BOOK AND HYMNAL. *Used by permission.*

in his Name, And with his Blood the Lamb of God
tears to see, With rap - ture bring your sheaves and sing

Hath washed a - way their shame. Be - fore God's face they
A heaven - ly mel - o - dy. Lift up your palms, your

sing and pray, Their voic - es blend with an-gels' lay, And
voic - es raise Through heav - en's vault and end-less days. To

all con-spire, a joy - ous choir, To laud him night and day.
God and to the Lamb is due E - ter - ni - ty of praise.

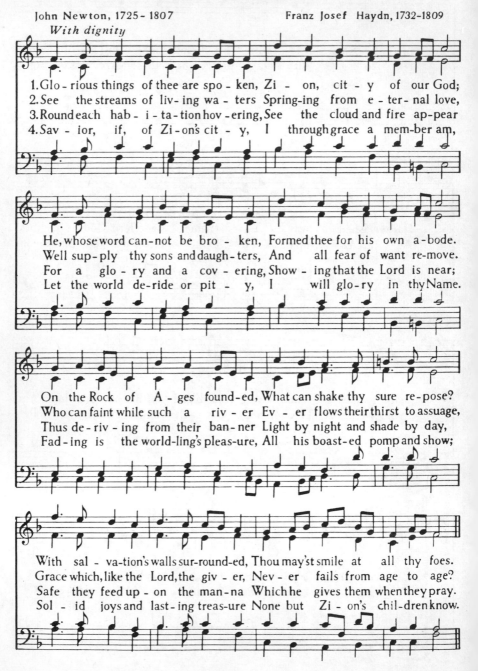

87 Glorious Things of Thee Are Spoken

AUSTRIAN HYMN. 87, 87. D.

John Newton, 1725-1807   Franz Josef Haydn, 1732-1809

With dignity

1. Glo-rious things of thee are spo-ken, Zi-on, cit-y of our God;
2. See the streams of liv-ing wa-ters Spring-ing from e-ter-nal love,
3. Round each hab-i-ta-tion hov-ering, See the cloud and fire ap-pear
4. Sav-ior, if, of Zi-on's cit-y, I through grace a mem-ber am,

He, whose word can-not be bro-ken, Formed thee for his own a-bode.
Well sup-ply thy sons and daugh-ters, And all fear of want re-move.
For a glo-ry and a cov-ering, Show-ing that the Lord is near;
Let the world de-ride or pit-y, I will glo-ry in thy Name.

On the Rock of A-ges found-ed, What can shake thy sure re-pose?
Who can faint while such a riv-er Ev-er flows their thirst to assuage,
Thus de-riv-ing from their ban-ner Light by night and shade by day,
Fad-ing is the world-ling's pleas-ure, All his boast-ed pomp and show;

With sal-va-tion's walls sur-round-ed, Thou may'st smile at all thy foes.
Grace which, like the Lord, the giv-er, Nev-er fails from age to age?
Safe they feed up-on the man-na Which he gives them when they pray.
Sol-id joys and last-ing treas-ure None but Zi-on's chil-dren know.

HEAVEN
In Heaven Above

HAUGE. 86, 86, 886.

Laurentius L. Laurinus, 1573-1655
Revised, Johan Åstrom, 1767-1844
Tr. William Maccall, 1812-1888

Norwegian Folk Melody

With movement

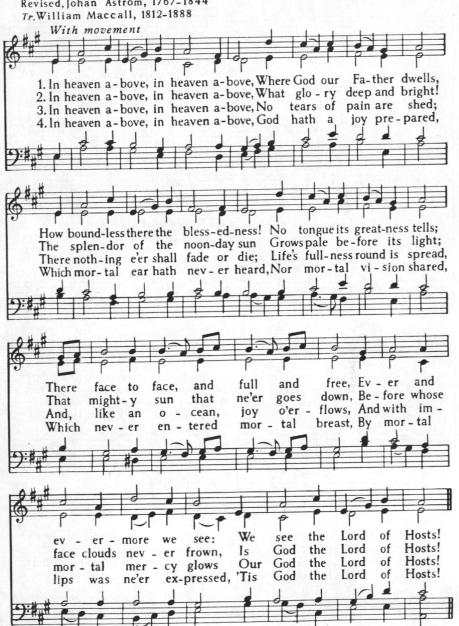

1. In heaven a-bove, in heaven a-bove, Where God our Fa-ther dwells,
2. In heaven a-bove, in heaven a-bove, What glo-ry deep and bright!
3. In heaven a-bove, in heaven a-bove, No tears of pain are shed;
4. In heaven a-bove, in heaven a-bove, God hath a joy pre-pared,

How bound-less there the bless-ed-ness! No tongue its great-ness tells;
The splen-dor of the noon-day sun Grows pale be-fore its light;
There noth-ing e'er shall fade or die; Life's full-ness round is spread,
Which mor-tal ear hath nev-er heard, Nor mor-tal vi-sion shared,

There face to face, and full and free, Ev-er and
That might-y sun that ne'er goes down, Be-fore whose
And, like an o-cean, joy o'er-flows, And with im-
Which nev-er en-tered mor-tal breast, By mor-tal

ev-er-more we see: We see the Lord of Hosts!
face clouds nev-er frown, Is God the Lord of Hosts!
mor-tal mer-cy glows Our God the Lord of Hosts!
lips was ne'er ex-pressed, 'Tis God the Lord of Hosts!

89 There's a Friend for Little Children

EDENGROVE. 86, 76, 76, 76.

Albert Midlane, 1825-1909   Samuel Smith, 1821-1917

Cheerfully

1. There's a Friend for lit - tle chil-dren A - bove the bright blue sky,
2. There's a rest for lit - tle chil-dren A - bove the bright blue sky,
3. There's a home for lit - tle chil-dren A - bove the bright blue sky,
4. There's a crown for lit - tle chil-dren A - bove the bright blue sky,

A Friend who nev - er chang-es, Whose love will nev - er die;
Who love the bless - ed Sav-ior, And to the Fa - ther cry;
Where Je - sus reigns in glo - ry, A home of peace and joy;
And all who look to Je - sus Shall wear it by and by;

Our earth-ly friends may fail us And change with chang-ing years,
A rest from ev - ery trou-ble, From sin and dan-ger free,
No home on earth is like it, Nor can with it com-pare;
A crown of bright-est glo - ry, Which he will then be - stow

This Friend is al - ways wor-thy Of that dear Name he bears.
Where ev - ery lit - tle pil-grim Shall rest e - ter - nal - ly.
For ev - ery one is hap-py, Nor could be hap-pier there.
On those who found his fa - vor, And loved his Name be - low.

SCHÖNSTER HERR JESU. 557, 558.

Münster Gesangbuch, 1677
Schlesische Volkslieder, 1842
Tr. Joseph A. Seiss, 1823-1904

Silesian Folksong, 1842

1. Beau - ti - ful Sav - ior, King of Cre - a - tion, Son of
2. Fair are the mead-ows, Fair are the wood-lands, Robed in
3. Fair is the sun-shine, Fair is the moon-light, Bright the
4. Beau - ti - ful Sav - ior, Lord of the na - tions, Son of

God and Son of Man! Tru-ly I'd love thee, Tru-ly I'd
flowers of bloom-ing spring; Je-sus is fair - er, Je-sus is
spark-ling stars on high; Je-sus shines bright-er, Je-sus shines
God and Son of Man! Glo-ry and hon - or, Praise, ad- o -

serve thee, Light of my soul, my joy, my crown.
pur - er, He makes our sor-rowing spir- it sing.
pur - er, Than all the an - gels in the sky.
ra - tion, Now and for ev - er - more be thine! A-men.

Beautiful Savior is a hymn that grows with us. We learn it in days of childhood, we sing it with fervent devotion in years of youth, and we come to treasure it more and more as we get older and older.

Its lines and words are simple and plain. But they are also very deep and profound. Here we worship Jesus in all his grace and beauty. But here we also confess and own him in all the fulness of his divine authority and power. He is "Son of God and Son of Man . . . King of creation . . . Lord of the nations . . . Light of my soul, my joy, my crown."

91 All Hail the Power of Jesus' Name

MILES LANE. C. M.

FIRST TUNE

Edward Perronet, 1726-1792
John Rippon, 1751-1836

William Shrubsole, 1760-1806

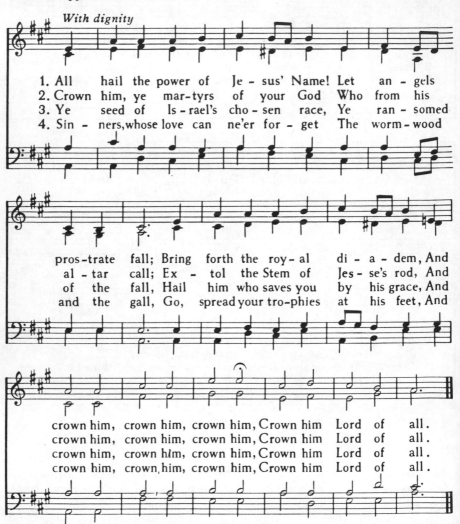

With dignity

1. All hail the power of Je - sus' Name! Let an - gels
2. Crown him, ye mar-tyrs of your God Who from his
3. Ye seed of Is - rael's cho - sen race, Ye ran - somed
4. Sin - ners, whose love can ne'er for - get The worm - wood

pros -trate fall; Bring forth the roy - al di - a - dem, And
al - tar call; Ex - tol the Stem of Jes - se's rod, And
of the fall, Hail him who saves you by his grace, And
and the gall, Go, spread your tro-phies at his feet, And

crown him, crown him, crown him, Crown him Lord of all.
crown him, crown him, crown him, Crown him Lord of all.
crown him, crown him, crown him, Crown him Lord of all.
crown him, crown, him, crown him, Crown him Lord of all.

5. Let every kindred, every tribe,
   On this terrestrial ball,
   To him all majesty ascribe,
   And crown him Lord of all.

6. O that with yonder sacred throng
   We at his feet may fall;
   We'll join the everlasting song
   And crown him Lord of all.

All Hail the Power of Jesus' Name 91

CORONATION. 86, 86, 86.

SECOND TUNE

Edward Perronet, 1726-1792
John Rippon, 1751-1836

Oliver Holden, 1765-1844

With dignity

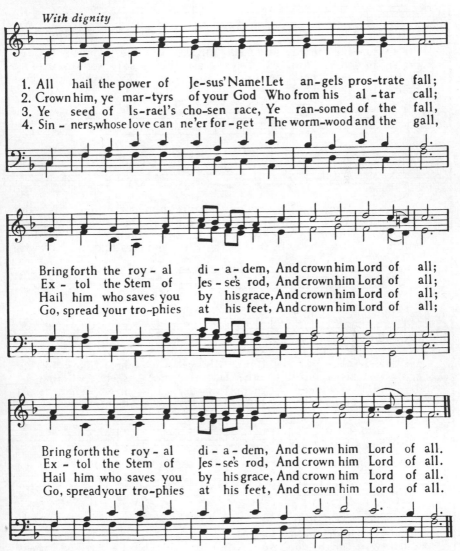

1. All hail the power of Je-sus' Name! Let an-gels pros-trate fall;
2. Crown him, ye mar-tyrs of your God Who from his al-tar call;
3. Ye seed of Is-rael's cho-sen race, Ye ran-somed of the fall,
4. Sin - ners, whose love can ne'er for-get The worm-wood and the gall,

Bring forth the roy - al di - a - dem, And crown him Lord of all;
Ex - tol the Stem of Jes - se's rod, And crown him Lord of all;
Hail him who saves you by his grace, And crown him Lord of all;
Go, spread your tro-phies at his feet, And crown him Lord of all;

Bring forth the roy - al di - a - dem, And crown him Lord of all.
Ex - tol the Stem of Jes - se's rod, And crown him Lord of all.
Hail him who saves you by his grace, And crown him Lord of all.
Go, spread your tro-phies at his feet, And crown him Lord of all.

5. Let every kindred, every tribe,
   On this terrestrial ball,
   To him all majesty ascribe,
   And crown him Lord of all.

6. O that with yonder sacred throng
   We at his feet may fall;
   We'll join the everlasting song
   And crown him Lord of all.

92 **Praise to the Lord**

LOBE DEN HERREN. 14, 14, 478.

Joachim Neander, 1650-1680
Tr. Catherine Winkworth, 1829-1878
Based on Psalms 103 and 150

Stralsund *Gesangbuch*, 1665

Majestically

1. Praise to the Lord, the Al - might - y, the King of Cre - a - tion; O my soul, praise him, for he is thy health and sal - va - tion: All ye who hear, Now to his tem - ple draw near; Join - ing in glad ad - o - ra - tion.

2. Praise to the Lord, who o'er all things so won - drous - ly reign - eth, Shel-ters thee un - der his wings, yea, so gen - tly sus - tain - eth: Hast thou not seen? All that is need-ful hath been Grant-ed in what he or - dain - eth.

3. Praise to the Lord, who doth pros - per thy work and de - fend thee; Sure-ly his good-ness and mer - cy here dai - ly at - tend thee. Pon-der a - new What the Al - might-y can do, If with his love he be - friend thee!

4. Praise to the Lord, O let all that is in me a - dore him; All that hath life and breath, come now with prais-es be - fore him! Let the A - men Sound from his peo-ple a - gain; Glad-ly for aye we a - dore him.

Immortal, Invisible, God Only Wise   93

ST. DENIO. 11 11, 11 11.

Walter C. Smith, 1824-1908   Welsh Hymn Melody

Majestically

1. Im - mor-tal, in - vis - i - ble, God on - ly wise,
2. Un - rest-ing, un - hast-ing, and si - lent as light,
3. To all life thou giv - est, to both great and small;
4. Great Fa-ther of glo - ry, pure Fa-ther of light,

In light in - ac - ces - si - ble hid from our eyes,
Nor want-ing, nor wast-ing, thou rul - est in might;
In all life thou liv - est, the true life of all;
Thine an-gels a - dore thee, all veil-ing their sight;

Most bless-ed, most glo-rious, the An - cient of Days,
Thy jus-tice like moun-tains high soar-ing a - bove,
We blos-som and flour-ish like leaves on the tree,
All laud we would ren-der: O help us to see

Al-might - y, vic - to-rious, thy great Name we praise.
Thy clouds which are foun-tains of good-ness and love.
And with - er and per-ish; but naught chang-eth thee.
'Tis on - ly the splen-dor of light hid - eth thee. A - men.

94 All Creatures of Our God and King

LASST UNS ERFREUEN. 88, 44, 88. With Refrain.

Francis of Assisi, 1182-1226

Geistliche Kirchengesänge, Cologne, 1623

Tr. William H. Draper, 1855-1933

Boldly

1. All crea-tures of our God and King, Lift up your voice and
2. Thou rush-ing wind that art so strong, Ye clouds that sail in
3. Thou flow-ing wa.- ter, pure and clear, Make mu-sic for thy
4. Dear moth-er earth, who day by day Un - fold-est bless-ings

with us sing, Al - le - lu - ia, al - le - lu - ia!
heaven a - long, O praise him, al - le - lu - ia!
Lord to hear, Al - le - lu - ia, al - le - lu - ia!
on our way, O praise him, al - le - lu - ia!

Thou burn-ing sun with gold-en beam, Thou sil-ver moon
Thou ris - ing morn, in praise re - joice, Ye lights of eve-
Thou fire so mas-ter- ful and bright, That giv-est man
The flowers and fruits that in thee grow, Let them his glo-

Refrain

with soft - er gleam:
ning, find a voice:
both warmth and light:
ry al - so show:

O praise him, O praise him,

Al-le - lu - ia, al - le - lu - ia, al - le - lu - - ia!

5. And all ye men of tender heart,
Forgiving others, take your part,
O sing ye, alleluia!
Ye who long pain and sorrow bear,
Praise God and on him cast your care:

6. And thou, most kind and gentle death,
Waiting to hush our latest breath,
O praise him, alleluia!
Thou leadest home the child of God,
And Christ our Lord the way hath trod:

7. Let all things their Creator bless,
And worship him in humbleness;
O praise him, alleluia!
Praise, praise the Father, praise the Son,
And praise the Spirit, Three in One:

Words by permission of J. Curwen and Sons, Ltd., London.
This hymn lends itself to antiphonal singing.

IHS is another monogram for one of the names of our Lord. Sometimes this monogram appears as IHC, meaning the same as IHS, only in a different style of lettering. In either form, this monogram is an abbreviation of ΙΗΣΟΥΣ, the Greek word for *Jesus*.

95　　**When Morning Gilds the Skies**

LAUDES DOMINI. 666, 666.

German Hymn, XIX *cent.*
Tr. Robert Bridges, 1844-1930

Joseph Barnby, 1838-1896

1. When morn-ing gilds the skies, My heart a-wak-ing cries,
2. When mirth for mu-sic longs, This is my song of songs,
3. To him, my highest and best, Sing I, when love-pos-sessed,
4. No love-lier an-ti-phon In all high heaven is known

May Jesus Christ be praised. When eve-ning shad-ows fall,
May Jesus Christ be praised. God's ho-ly house of prayer
May Jesus Christ be praised. What-e'er my hands be-gin,
Than 'Jesus Christ be praised'. There to the e-ter-nal Word

This rings my cur-few call, May Jesus Christ be praised.
Hath none that can com-pare With 'Jesus Christ be praised'.
This bless-ing break-eth in, May Jesus Christ be praised.
The e-ter-nal psalm is heard, 'O Jesus Christ be praised'.

5. Ye nations of mankind,
In this your concord find,
May Jesus Christ be praised.
Let all the earth around
Ring joyous with the sound,
May Jesus Christ be praised.

6. Sing, suns and stars of space,
Sing, ye that see his face,
Sing, 'Jesus Christ be praised'.
God's whole creation o'er,
For aye and evermore
Shall Jesus Christ be praised.

From THE YATTENDON HYMNAL, *edited by Robert Bridges, by permission of Oxford University Press, London.*

Shepherd of Tender Youth

OLIVET. 664, 6664.

Clement of Alexandria, *ctr.* 170
Tr. Henry M. Dexter, 1821-1890

Lowell Mason, 1792-1872

In moderate time

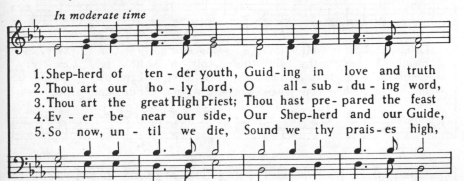

1. Shep-herd of ten - der youth, Guid-ing in love and truth
2. Thou art our ho - ly Lord, O all - sub - du - ing word,
3. Thou art the great High Priest; Thou hast pre - pared the feast
4. Ev - er be near our side, Our Shep-herd and our Guide,
5. So now, un - til we die, Sound we thy prais - es high,

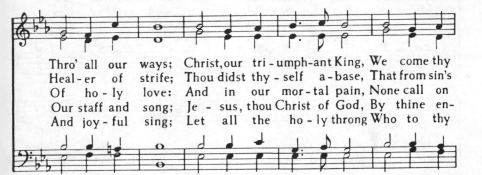

Thro' all our ways; Christ, our tri - umph-ant King, We come thy
Heal - er of strife; Thou didst thy - self a - base, That from sin's
Of ho - ly love: And in our mor - tal pain, None call on
Our staff and song; Je - sus, thou Christ of God, By thine en-
And joy - ful sing; Let all the ho - ly throng Who to thy

Name to sing, And here our chil-dren bring Their hymns of praise.
deep dis-grace Thou might-est save our race, And give us life.
thee in vain; Help thou dost not dis-dain, Help from a - bove.
dur - ing word, Lead us where thou hast trod, Make our faith strong.
church be-long, U - nite and swell the song To Christ, our King! A-men.

97 Love Divine, All Loves Excelling

HYFRYDOL. 87, 87. D.

Charles Wesley, 1707-1788

Rowland H. Prichard, 1811-1887

In moderate time

1. Love di - vine, all loves ex - cel - ling, Joy of heaven, to
2. Breathe, O breathe thy lov - ing spir - it In - to ev - ery
3. Come, al - might - y to de - liv - er, Let us all thy
4. Fin - ish then thy new cre - a - tion, Pure and spot - less

earth come down! Fix in us thy hum - ble dwell-ing, All thy
trou - bled breast; Let us all in thee in - her - it, Let us
life re - ceive; Sud - den - ly re - turn, and nev - er, Nev - er
let us be; Let us see thy great sal - va - tion Per - fect-

faith - ful mer - cies crown. Je - sus, thou art all com - pas-sion,
find thy prom - ised rest. Take a - way the love of sin - ning;
more thy tem - ples leave. Thee we would be al - ways bless - ing,
ly re - stored in thee! Changed from glo - ry in - to glo - ry,

Pure un - bound - ed love thou art; Vis - it us with
Al - pha and O - me - ga be; End of faith, as
Serve thee as thy hosts a - bove, Pray, and praise thee
Till in heaven we take our place, Till we cast our

thy sal - va - tion, En - ter ev - ery trem-bling heart.
its be - gin - ning, Set our hearts at lib - er - ty.
with - out ceas - ing, Glo-ry in thy pre-cious love.
crowns be - fore thee, Lost in won-der, love, and praise. A-men.

My God, How Wonderful Thou Art   98
DUNDEE (FRENCH). C. M.

Frederick W. Faber, 1814-1863   *Scottish Psalter*, 1615

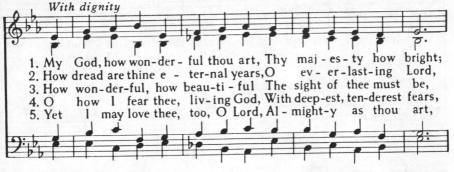

With dignity

1. My God, how won-der - ful thou art, Thy maj - es - ty how bright;
2. How dread are thine e - ter-nal years, O ev - er-last-ing Lord,
3. How won-der-ful, how beau-ti - ful The sight of thee must be,
4. O how I fear thee, liv-ing God, With deep-est, ten-derest fears,
5. Yet I may love thee, too, O Lord, Al - might-y as thou art,

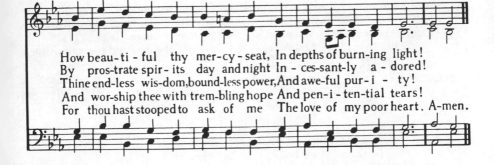

How beau-ti - ful thy mer-cy - seat, In depths of burn-ing light!
By pros-trate spir - its day and night In - ces-sant-ly a - dored!
Thine end-less wis-dom, bound-less power, And awe-ful pur-i - ty!
And wor-ship thee with trem-bling hope And pen-i - ten-tial tears!
For thou hast stooped to ask of me The love of my poor heart. A-men.

6. No earthly father loves like thee;
No mother, e'er so mild,
Bears and forbears as thou hast done
With me, thy sinful child.

7. Father of Jesus, love's reward,
What rapture will it be
Prostrate before thy throne to lie,
And gaze and gaze on thee!

99 O Worship the King

Robert Grant, 1779-1838
Based on Psalm 104

HANOVER. 10 10, 11 11.

William Croft, 1678-1727

With dignity

1. O wor-ship the King, all glo-rious a-bove, O grate-ful-ly sing his won-der-ful love; Our shield and de-fend-er, the An-cient of Days, Pa-vil-ioned in splen-dor, and gird-ed with praise.

2. O tell of his might, O sing of his grace, Whose robe is the light, whose can-o-py space; His char-iots of wrath the deep thun-der-clouds form, And dark is his path on the wings of the storm.

3. The earth with its store of won-ders un-told, Al-might-y, thy power hath found-ed of old; Hath stab-lished it fast by a change-less de-cree, And round it hath cast, like a man-tle, the sea.

4. Thy boun-ti-ful care what tongue can re-cite? It breathes in the air, it shines in the light; It streams from the hills, it de-scends to the plain, And sweet-ly dis-tills in the dew and the rain. A-men.

5. Frail children of dust, and feeble as frail,
In thee do we trust, nor find thee to fail;
Thy mercies how tender, how firm to the end,
Our Maker, Defender, Redeemer, and Friend.

6. O measureless Might, ineffable Love,
While angels delight to hymn thee above,
The humbler creation, though feeble their lays,
With true adoration shall sing to thy praise.

Praise, My Soul, the King of Heaven   100

OUR LADY, TRONDHJEM. 87, 87, 87.

Henry F. Lyte, 1793-1847
Based on Psalm 103

Ludvig M. Lindeman, 1812-1887

With dignity

1. Praise, my soul, the King of heav - en; To his feet thy
2. Praise him for his grace and fa - vor To our fa - thers
3. Fa - ther-like he tends and spares us, Well our fee - ble
4. An - gels, help us to a - dore him, Ye be - hold him

trib - ute bring; Ran-somed, healed, re - stored, for - giv - en,
in dis - tress; Praise him, still the same for ev - er,
frame he knows; In his hands he gent - ly bears us,
face to face; Sun and moon, bow down be - fore him;

Who like me his praise should sing? Al - le - lu - ia!
Slow to chide, and swift to bless: Al - le - lu - ia!
Res - cues us from all our foes: Al - le - lu - ia!
Dwell-ers all in time and space: Al - le - lu - ia!

Al - le - lu - ia! Praise the ev - er - last - ing King.
Al - le - lu - ia! Glo - rious in his faith - ful - ness.
Al - le - lu - ia! Wide - ly as his mer - cy flows.
Al - le - lu - ia! Praise with us the God of grace.

OPENING

101 Look upon Us, Blessed Lord

LIEBSTER JESU, WIR SIND HIER (DESSAU). 78, 78, 88.

Tobias Clausnitzer, 1619-1684
Tr. Robert A. S. Macalister, 1870-1950, *alt.*

Johann R. Ahle, 1625-1673

With movement

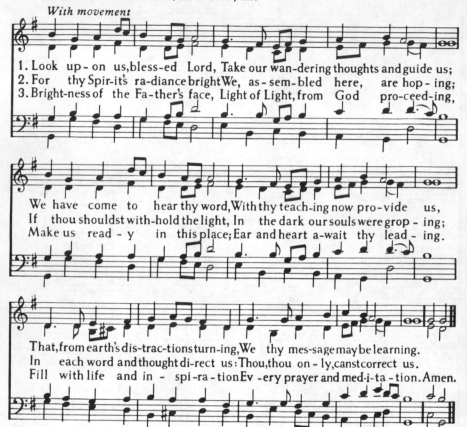

1. Look up-on us, bless-ed Lord, Take our wan-dering thoughts and guide us;
2. For thy Spir-it's ra-diance bright We, as-sem-bled here, are hop-ing;
3. Bright-ness of the Fa-ther's face, Light of Light, from God pro-ceed-ing,

We have come to hear thy word, With thy teach-ing now pro-vide us,
If thou shouldst with-hold the light, In the dark our souls were grop-ing;
Make us read-y in this place; Ear and heart a-wait thy lead-ing.

That, from earth's dis-trac-tions turn-ing, We thy mes-sage may be learning.
In each word and thought di-rect us: Thou, thou on-ly, canst correct us.
Fill with life and in-spi-ra-tion Ev-ery prayer and med-i-ta-tion. Amen.

Words from the SERVICE BOOK AND HYMNAL. Used by permission.

102 I Worship Thee, Lord Jesus

ACH BLEIB MIT DEINER GNADE. 76, 76.

Richard F. Littledale, 1833-1890

Melchior Vulpius, *ctr.* 1560-1615

Simply

1. I wor-ship thee, Lord Je-sus, As chil-dren did of old,
2. I wor-ship thee, Lord Je-sus, My King and Sav-ior mild:

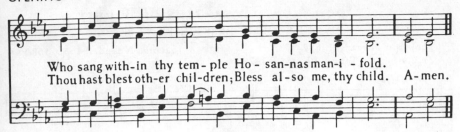

Who sang with-in thy tem - ple Ho - san-nas man-i - fold.
Thou hast blest oth-er chil-dren; Bless al-so me, thy child. A-men.

Lord Jesus Christ, Be Present Now   103
HERR JESU CHRIST, DICH ZU UNS WEND.   L. M.

Wilhelm II, Duke of Saxe-Weimar, 1598-1662   *Pensum Sacrum*, Görlitz, 1648
Tr. Catherine Winkworth, 1829-1878, *alt.*

Stately

1. Lord Je - sus Christ, be pres - ent now, And
2. Our voic - es tune to sing thy praise, Our
3. Then shall we join the hosts that cry, Thrice -
4. Glo - ry to God, the Fa - ther, Son, And

let thy Ho - ly Spir - it bow All hearts in love and
hearts in true de - vo-tion raise, Our faith in-crease, and
ho - ly is the Lord Most High! And dwell with God in
Ho - ly Spir - it, Three in One; To thee, O bless - ed

fear to-day, To hear the truth and keep thy way.
grant us light That we may know thy Name a - right.
that blest place Where we shall see him face to face.
Trin - i - ty, Be praise through-out e - ter - ni - ty! A - men.

104 Open Now Thy Gates of Beauty

NEANDER (UNSER HERRSCHER). 87, 87, 77.

Benjamin Schmolck, 1672-1737
Tr. Catherine Winkworth, 1829-1878

Joachim Neander, 1650-1680

With dignity

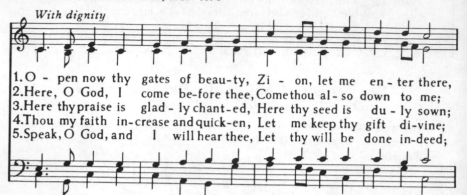

1. O - pen now thy gates of beau-ty, Zi - on, let me en - ter there,
2. Here, O God, I come be-fore thee, Come thou al - so down to me;
3. Here thy praise is glad - ly chant-ed, Here thy seed is du - ly sown;
4. Thou my faith in-crease and quick-en, Let me keep thy gift di-vine;
5. Speak, O God, and I will hear thee, Let thy will be done in-deed;

Where my soul in joy-ful du - ty Waits on him who an-swers prayer:
Where we find thee and a-dore thee, There a heaven on earth must be:
Let my soul, where it is plant-ed, Bring forth pre-cious sheaves a - lone:
How-so-e'er temp-ta-tions thick-en, May thy word still o'er me shine,
May I un-dis-turbed draw near thee While thou dost thy peo-ple feed;

O how bless-ed is this place, Filled with sol-ace, light, and grace.
To my heart O en - ter thou, Let it be thy tem-ple now.
So that all I hear may be Fruit-ful un - to life in me.
As my guid-ing star through life, As my com-fort in my strife.
Here of life the foun-tain flows, Here is balm for all our woes. A-men.

RATISBON. 77, 77, 77.

Charles Wesley, 1707-1788   Werner's *Choralbuch*, 1815

In moderate time

1. Christ, whose glo-ry fills the skies, Christ the true, the on-ly Light,
2. Dark and cheer-less is the morn Un - ac-com-pa - nied by thee;
3. Vis - it then this soul of mine; Pierce the gloom of sin and grief;

Sun of Right-eous-ness, a - rise, Tri-umph o'er the shades of night;
Joy-less is the day's re-turn Till thy mer-cy's beams I see;
Fill me, Ra-dian - cy di-vine, Scat-ter all my un - be-lief;

Day-spring from on high, be near; Day-star, in my heart ap-pear.
Till they in-ward light im-part, Glad my eyes, and warm my heart.
More and more thy-self dis-play, Shin-ing to the per-fect day. A-men.

This hymn may also be sung to DIX (No. 44), or EASTER GLORY (No. 63).

Beginnings are important.

If you begin each day with a groan and a sigh, without a thought of God or Christ—then many of your days will be as dark and cheerless as this rich and beautiful morning hymn says.

But if you begin each day with a song and a prayer, with your eyes open to Christ—then in rain or shine, summer or winter, your days will be different. They will then begin as real "Good Mornings" with the grace and goodness of God in your heart.

106 ## Lord, Dismiss Us with Thy Blessing

SICILIAN MARINERS. 87, 87, 87.

John Fawcett, 1740-1817   Sicilian Melody, XVIII cent.

In moderate time

1. Lord, dis-miss us with thy bless-ing, Fill our hearts with joy and peace;
2. Thanks we give and ad-o-ra-tion For thy Gos-pel's joy-ful sound;

Let us each, thy love pos-sess-ing, Tri-umph in re-deem-ing grace.
May the fruits of thy sal-va-tion In our hearts and lives a-bound;

O re-fresh us, O re-fresh us, Trav'-ling thro' this wil-der-ness.
Ev-er faith-ful, ev-er faith-ful To thy truth may we be found. Amen.

This hymn may also be sung to REGENT SQUARE *(No. 79).*

107 ## Almighty Father, Bless the Word

Tune: OLD HUNDREDTH (No. 116).

1. Almighty Father, bless the word
   Which through thy grace we now have heard.
   Oh, may the precious seed take root,
   Spring up, and bear abundant fruit!

2. We praise thee for the means of grace
   As homeward now our steps we trace.
   Grant, Lord, that we who worship here
   May all at last in heaven appear. Amen.

From the Scandinavian,
Author unknown

Savior, Again to Thy Dear Name We Raise 108

ELLERS. 10 10, 10 10.

John Ellerton, 1826-1893

Edward J. Hopkins, 1818-1901

In moderate time

1. Sav - ior, a - gain to thy dear Name we raise
2. Grant us thy peace up - on our home - ward way;
3. Grant us thy peace, Lord, through the com - ing night,
4. Grant us thy peace through - out our earth - ly life,

With one ac - cord our part - ing hymn of praise;
With thee be - gan, with thee shall end the day;
Turn thou for us its dark - ness in - to light;
Our balm in sor - row, and our stay in strife;

Once more we bless thee ere our wor - ship cease,
Guard thou the lips from sin, the hearts from shame,
From harm and dan - ger keep thy chil - dren free,
Then, when thy voice shall bid our con - flict cease,

Then, low - ly bend - ing, wait thy word of peace.
That in this house have called up - on thy Name.
For dark and light are both a - like to thee.
Call us, O Lord, to thine e - ter - nal peace. A - men.

109 Abide with Us, Our Savior

ACH BLEIB MIT DEINER GNADE. 76, 76.

Josua Stegmann, 1588-1632
Tr. Unknown

Melchior Vulpius, ctr. 1560-1615

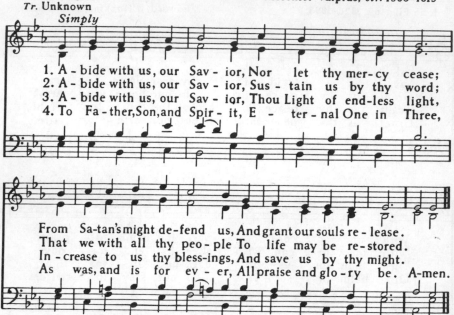

Simply

1. A - bide with us, our Sav - ior, Nor let thy mer-cy cease;
2. A - bide with us, our Sav - ior, Sus - tain us by thy word;
3. A - bide with us, our Sav - ior, Thou Light of end-less light,
4. To Fa-ther, Son, and Spir - it, E - ter - nal One in Three,

From Sa-tan's might de-fend us, And grant our souls re - lease.
That we with all thy peo-ple To life may be re-stored.
In - crease to us thy bless-ings, And save us by thy might.
As was, and is for ev - er, All praise and glo-ry be. A-men.

110 On Our Way Rejoicing

Tune: HERMAS (No. 70).

1. On our way rejoicing
Gladly let us go;
Conquered hath our Leader,
Vanquished is the foe.
Christ without, our safety;
Christ within, our joy;
Who, if we be faithful,
Can our hope destroy?

2. If with honest - hearted
Love for God and man,
Day by day thou find us
Doing what we can,
Thou who giv'st the seedtime
Wilt give large increase,
Crown the head with blessings,
Fill the heart with peace.

3. Unto God the Father
Joyful songs we sing,
Unto God the Savior
Thankful hearts we bring,
Unto God the Spirit
Bow we and adore,
On our way rejoicing
Now and evermore.

Refrain. On our way rejoicing
As we forward move,
Hearken to our praises,
O thou God of love! Amen.

John S. B. Monsell, 1811-1875

Praise to Thee and Adoration

111

PSALM 42 (FREU DICH SEHR). 87, 87, 77, 88.

Thomas H. Kingo, 1634-1703
Tr. Kristen Kvamme, 1866-1938, *alt.*

Genevan Psalter, 1551
Adapt. and harm. J. S. Bach, 1685-1750

Brightly

1. Praise to thee and ad - o - ra - tion, Bless - ed Je - sus,
2. Let me nev - er, Lord, for - sake thee, E'en though bit - ter

Son of God, Who, to serve thine own cre - a - tion,
pain and strife On my way should o - ver - take me;

Didst as-sume our flesh and blood. Grant that I may nev - er stray,
But may I through all my life Walk in fer-vent love to thee,

From thy sa - cred fold a - way, But with zeal and ho - ly fa -
In all woes for com-fort flee To thy birth, thy death and pas -

vor Fol - low thee, O bless - ed Sav - ior.
sion, Till I see thy full sal - va - tion. A - men.

EVENING
Abide with Me
EVENTIDE. 10 10, 10 10.

Henry F. Lyte, 1793-1847　　　　　　　　William H. Monk, 1823-1889

In moderate time

1. A - bide with me, fast falls the e - ven - tide;
2. Swift to its close ebbs out life's lit - tle day;
3. I need thy pres - ence ev - ery pass - ing hour;
4. I fear no foe, with thee at hand to bless;
5. Hold thou thy Cross be - fore my clos - ing eyes,

The dark - ness deep - ens, Lord, with me a - bide;
Earth's joys grow dim, its glo - ries pass a - way;
What but thy grace can foil the temp-ter's power?
Ills have no weight, and tears no bit - ter - ness.
Shine through the gloom, and point me to the skies;

When oth - er help - ers fail and com - forts flee,
Change and de - cay in all a - round I see;
Who like thy - self my guide and stay can be?
Where is death's sting? Where, grave, thy vic - to - ry?
Heaven's morn - ing breaks, and earth's vain shad - ows flee;

Help of the help-less, O a - bide with me.
O thou who chang-est not, a - bide with me.
Through cloud and sun-shine, O a - bide with me.
I tri - umph still, if thou a - bide with me.
In life, in death, O Lord, a - bide with me. A-men.

Now Rest Beneath Night's Shadow   113

INNSBRUCK. 776, 778.

Paul Gerhardt, 1607-1676

Heinrich Isaak, *ctr.* 1450-1527

Tr. Catherine Winkworth, 1829-1878 *Harm.* F. Melius Christiansen, 1871-1955

Now rest be-neath night's shad-ow The wood-land, field, and mead-ow,

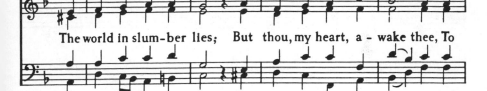

The world in slum-ber lies; But thou, my heart, a - wake thee, To

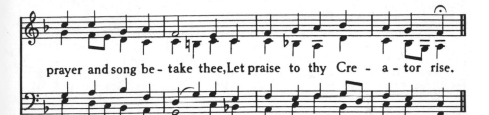

prayer and song be - take thee, Let praise to thy Cre - a - tor rise.

Harmonization from The Lutheran Hymnary, *copyright Augsburg Publishing House.*

Morning and evening. Day and night.

All time is God's time. All time is time God gives us for living as his children.

One of the best times to think about this is when we go to bed. In those quiet moments before we go to sleep we have a good time to think of God's grace and his will for us—to breathe our prayers of thanksgiving and confession. This is also a good time to sing one of the fine evening hymns of the church—and then go to sleep with the prayer of the psalmist: "In peace I will both lie down and sleep; for thou alone, O Lord, makest me dwell in safety" (Psalm 4:8).

114 All Praise to Thee, My God, This Night

TALLIS' CANON. L. M.

Thomas Ken, 1637-1711, *alt.*   Thomas Tallis, *ctr.* 1505-1585

With dignity

1. All praise to thee, my God, this night, For all the
2. For - give me, Lord, for thy dear Son, The ill that
3. Teach me to live, that I may dread The grave as
4. O when shall I, in end-less day, For ev - er
5. Praise God, from whom all bless-ings flow; Praise him, all

bless-ings of the light; Keep me, O keep me, King of Kings,
I this day have done, That with the world, my - self, and thee,
lit - tle as my bed; Teach me to die, that so I may
chase dark sleep a - way, And hymns di-vine with an-gels sing
crea-tures here be - low; Praise him a-bove, ye heaven-ly host;

Be - neath thine own al - might - y wings!
I, ere I sleep, at peace may be.
Rise glo - rious at the awe - ful day.
In end - less praise to thee, my King?
Praise Fa - ther, Son, and Ho - ly Ghost. A - men.

This hymn may be sung in canon style.

Now the Day Is Over

MERRIAL. 65, 65.

Sabine Baring-Gould, 1834-1924 · Joseph Barnby, 1838-1896

Quietly

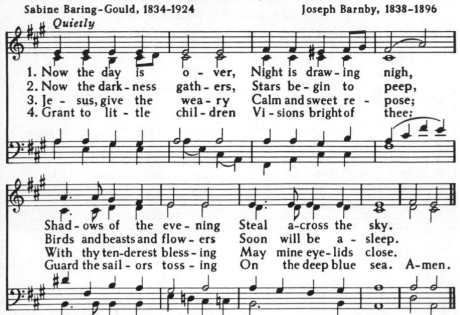

1. Now the day is o - ver, Night is draw - ing nigh,
2. Now the dark - ness gath - ers, Stars be - gin to peep,
3. Je - sus, give the wea - ry Calm and sweet re - pose;
4. Grant to lit - tle chil - dren Vi - sions bright of thee;

Shad - ows of the eve - ning Steal a - cross the sky.
Birds and beasts and flow - ers Soon will be a - sleep.
With thy ten-derest bless - ing May mine eye - lids close.
Guard the sail - ors toss - ing On the deep blue sea. A - men.

5. Comfort every sufferer
   Watching late in pain;
   Those who plan some evil
   From their sin restrain.

6. Through the long night -watches
   May thine angels spread
   Their white wings above me,
   Watching round my bed.

7. When the morning wakens,
   Then may I arise
   Pure and fresh and sinless
   In thy holy eyes,

8. Glory to the Father,
   Glory to the Son,
   And to thee, blest Spirit,
   Whilst all ages run.

Words by permission of J. Curwen and Son, Ltd., London.
This hymn may also be sung to ST. LUCIAN *(No. 189)*

All Praise to Thee, the evening hymn on the opposite page, is sort of a grown-up *Now I Lay Me Down to Sleep*.

Bishop Ken wrote this hymn and the morning hymn, *Awake, My Soul*, when he was headmaster of an English boys' school. For the closing stanzas of both hymns he wrote the lines of the *Doxology*—"Praise God from whom all blessings flow. . . ."

These hymns remind us that praise to God is the beginning and ending of our Christian faith and life. As we now live, we praise God for his grace and providence morning and evening, day and night. Then in the life to come this shall be our everlasting joy—to praise God in the never-ending days of eternity.

THE HOUSE OF GOD

116

How Blessed Is This Place

OLD HUNDREDTH. L.M.

Ernest E. Ryden, 1886-

Louis Bourgeois, *ctr.* 1510–1561
Genevan Psalter, 1551

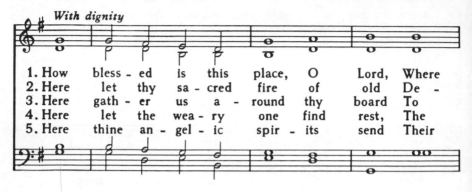

With dignity

1. How bless - ed is this place, O Lord, Where
2. Here let thy sa - cred fire of old De -
3. Here gath - er us a - round thy board To
4. Here let the wea - ry one find rest, The
5. Here thine an - gel - ic spir - its send Their

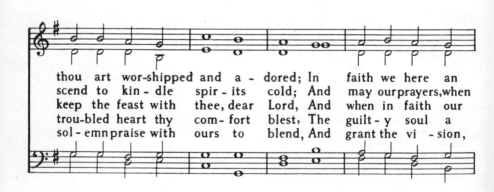

thou art wor-shipped and a - dored; In faith we here an
scend to kin - dle spir - its cold; And may our prayers, when
keep the feast with thee, dear Lord, And when in faith our
trou-bled heart thy com - fort blest, The guilt - y soul a
sol - emn praise with ours to blend, And grant the vi - sion,

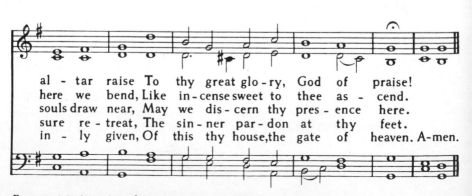

al - tar raise To thy great glo - ry, God of praise!
here we bend, Like in-cense sweet to thee as - cend.
souls draw near, May we dis - cern thy pres - ence here.
sure re - treat, The sin - ner par - don at thy feet.
in - ly given, Of this thy house, the gate of heaven. A-men.

For a metrical version of this hymn, see No. 235.

THE WORD OF GOD
Holy Bible, Book Divine

POSEN. 77, 77.

John Burton, 1803-1877, *alt.*

Georg C. Strattner, 1650-1705

In moderate time

1. Ho - ly Bi - ble, book di - vine, Pre- cious treas-ure, thou art mine;
2. Mine to com-fort in dis-tress, If the Ho - ly Spir- it bless;
3. Mine to tell of joys to come, Light and life be - yond the tomb.

Mine to tell me whence I came, Mine to teach me what I am;
Mine to show by liv-ing faith Man can tri-umph o-ver death;
Ho - ly Bi - ble, book di - vine, Pre-cious treas-ure, thou art mine.

"Thy word is a lamp to my feet and a light to my path" (Psalm 119: 105). The lamp is a symbol of Scripture as the Word of God. The idea of light often appears in the Bible. As John points out, Christ himself is the true Light: "In him was life, and the life was the light of men. The light shines in the darkness, and the darkness has not overcome it" (John 1:4-5).

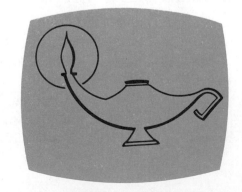

118 O Bread of Life from Heaven

INNSBRUCK. 776, 778.

Latin hymn, *ctr.* 1661
Tr. St. 1-2, Philip Schaff, 1819-1893
Tr. St. 3, Athelstan Riley, 1858-1945

Heinrich Isaak, *ctr.* 1450-1527
Harm. F. Melius Christiansen, 1871-1955

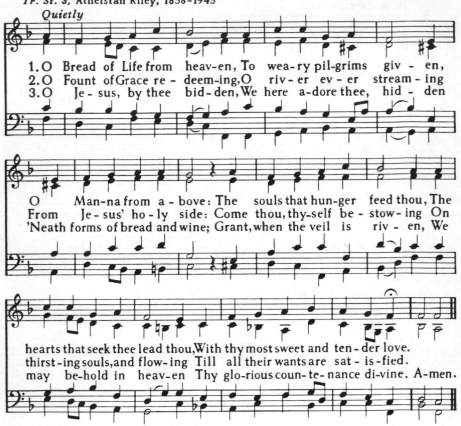

1. O Bread of Life from heav-en, To wea-ry pil-grims giv - en, O Man-na from a - bove: The souls that hun-ger feed thou, The hearts that seek thee lead thou, With thy most sweet and ten - der love.

2. O Fount of Grace re - deem-ing, O riv-er ev - er stream - ing From Je - sus' ho - ly side: Come thou, thy-self be - stow- ing On thirst-ing souls, and flow-ing Till all their wants are sat - is - fied.

3. O Je - sus, by thee bid-den, We here a-dore thee, hid - den 'Neath forms of bread and wine; Grant, when the veil is riv - en, We may be-hold in heav-en Thy glo-rious coun-te-nance di-vine. A-men.

God graciously comes to us through his Word and the Sacraments of Holy Baptism and Holy Communion.

O Bread of Life from Heaven is a prayer-hymn we often sing as we come to Holy Communion. Through the bread and wine in Holy Communion our Lord Jesus Christ comes to us. Here he gives us his Body and Blood which he gave and shed for us in his redeeming death on the Cross—that we may have the forgiveness of sins, life, and salvation.

Thy Word, O Lord, Like Gentle Dews   119

RELEASE. C. M. D.

Carl B. Garve, 1763-1841
Tr. Catherine Winkworth, 1829-1878

Danish Melody

Broadly

1. Thy Word, O Lord, like   gen-tle dews, Falls soft on hearts that pine;
2. Thy Word is like a   flam-ing sword, A wedge that cleav-eth stone;
3. Thy Word, a won-drous guid-ing star, On pil-grim hearts doth rise,

Lord, to thy gar-den ne'er re-fuse This heaven-ly balm of thine.
Keen as a fire, so burns thy Word, And pierc-eth flesh and bone.
Leads those to God who dwell a - far, And makes the sim-ple wise.

Wa-tered by thee, let ev-ery tree Then blos-som to thy praise,
Let it go forth o'er all the earth To cleanse our hearts with-in,
Let not its light e'er sink in night, But in each spir- it shine,

By grace of thine bear fruit di-vine Through all the com-ing days.
To show thy power in Sa-tan's hour, And break the might of sin.
That none may miss heaven's fi-nal bliss, Led by thy light di-vine. A-men.

120 ## O Word of God Incarnate

MUNICH (MEININGEN). 76, 76. D.

William W. How, 1823-1897

Meiningen Gesangbuch, 1693

Adapt and harm. Felix Mendelssohn, 1809-1847

In moderate time

1. O Word of God In-car-nate, O Wis-dom from on high,
2. The church from her dear Mas-ter Re-ceived the gift di-vine,
3. It float-eth like a ban-ner Be-fore God's host un-furled;
4. O make thy church, dear Sav-ior, A lamp of bur-nished gold,

O Truth un-changed, un-chang-ing, O Light of our dark sky;
And still that light she lift-eth O'er all the earth to shine.
It shin-eth like a bea-con A-bove the dark-ling world;
To bear be-fore the na-tions Thy true light, as of old;

We praise thee for the ra-diance That from the hal-lowed page,
It is the gold-en cas-ket Where gems of truth are stored;
It is the chart and com-pass That o'er life's surg-ing sea,
O teach thy wan-dering pil-grims By this their path to trace,

A lan-tern to our foot-steps, Shines on from age to age.
It is the heaven-drawn pic-ture Of Christ, the liv-ing Word.
'Mid mists and rocks and quick-sands, Still guides, O Christ, to thee.
Till, clouds and dark-ness end-ed, They see thee face to face. A-men.

God's Word Is Our Great Heritage

EIN' FESTE BURG. 87, 87, 66, 667.

Nikolai F. S. Grundtvig, 1783-1872
Tr. Ole G. Belsheim, 1861-1925, alt.

Martin Luther, 1483-1546

With vigor

God's Word is our great her - it - age, And shall be ours for ev - er; To spread its light from age to age Be this our chief en-deav - or; Through life it guides our way, In death it is our stay; Lord, grant while time shall last, Thy church may hold it fast Through-out all gen-er-a - tions. A-men.

MISSIONS

Christ for the World We Sing

CUTTING. 664, 6664.

Samuel Wolcott, 1813-1886

William F. Sherwin, 1826-1888

In moderate time

1. Christ for the world we sing; The world to
2. Christ for the world we sing; The world to
3. Christ for the world we sing; The world to
4. Christ for the world we sing; The world to

Christ we bring With lov-ing zeal; The poor and
Christ we bring With fer-vent prayer; The way-ward
Christ we bring With one ac-cord; With us the
Christ we bring With joy-ful song; The new-born

them that mourn, The faint and o-ver-borne,
and the lost, By rest-less pas-sions tossed,
work to share, With us re-proach to dare,
souls, whose days, Re-claimed from er-ror's ways,

rit.

Sin-sick and sor-row-worn, Whom Christ doth heal.
Re-deemed at count-less cost From dark de-spair.
With us the cross to bear, For Christ our Lord.
In-spired with hope and praise, To Christ be-long.

This hymn may be sung to MOSCOW (No. 82).

Hail to the Brightness of Zion's Glad Morning 123

WESLEY. 11 10, 11 10.

Thomas Hastings, 1784-1872, *alt.*   Lowell Mason, 1792-1872

With spirit

1. Hail to the bright-ness of Zi-on's glad morn-ing,
2. Hail to the bright-ness of Zi-on's glad morn-ing,
3. Lo, in the des-ert rich flow-ers are spring-ing,
4. See, from all lands, from the isles of the o-cean,

Joy to the lands that in dark-ness have lain!
Long by the proph-ets of Is-rael fore-told;
Streams ev-er co-pious are flow-ing a-long;
Praise to the Sav-ior as-cend-ing on high;

Hushed be the ac-cents of sor-row and mourn-ing,
Hail to the mil-lions from bond-age re-turn-ing,
Loud from the moun-tain-tops ech-oes are ring-ing,
Fall-en the weap-ons of war and com-mo-tion,

Zi-on in tri-umph be-gins her mild reign.
Gen-tiles and Jews the blest vi-sion be-hold.
Wastes rise in ver-dure and min-gle in song.
Shouts of sal-va-tion are rend-ing the sky.

124   I Love to Tell the Story

HANKEY. 76, 76. D. With Refrain.

Katherine Hankey, 1834-1911   William G. Fischer, 1835-1912

In moderate time

1. I love to tell the sto - ry Of un-seen things a - bove,
2. I love to tell the sto - ry, 'Tis pleas-ant to re - peat
3. I love to tell the sto - ry, For those who know it best

Of Je - sus and his glo - ry, Of Je - sus and his love.
What seems, each time I tell it, More won - der - ful - ly sweet.
Seem hun - ger - ing and thirst - ing To hear it like the rest.

I love to tell the sto - ry, Be - cause I know it's true;
I love to tell the sto - ry, For some have nev - er heard
And when, in scenes of glo - ry, I sing the new, new song,

It sat - is - fies my long-ings As noth-ing else would do.
The mes-sage of sal - va-tion From God's own ho - ly Word.
'Twill be the old, old sto - ry, That I have loved so long.

Refrain

I love to tell the sto-ry; 'Twill be my theme in glo-ry

To tell the old, old sto-ry Of Je-sus and his love.

Fling Out the Banner 125
WALTHAM. L. M.

George W. Doane, 1799-1859   John B. Calkin, 1827-1905

With spirit

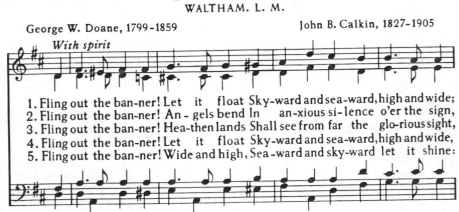

1. Fling out the ban-ner! Let it float Sky-ward and sea-ward, high and wide;
2. Fling out the ban-ner! An - gels bend In an-xious si-lence o'er the sign,
3. Fling out the ban-ner! Hea-then lands Shall see from far the glo-rious sight,
4. Fling out the ban-ner! Let it float Sky-ward and sea-ward, high and wide,
5. Fling out the ban-ner! Wide and high, Sea-ward and sky-ward let it shine:

The sun that lights its shin-ing folds, The Cross on which the Sav-ior died.
And vain-ly seek to com-pre-hend The won-der of the love di-vine.
And na-tions, crowd-ing to be born, Bap-tize their spir-its in its light.
Our glo-ry, on - ly in the Cross, Our on - ly hope, the Cru-ci-fied.
Nor skill, nor might, nor mer-it ours; We con-quer on - ly in that sign.

126 O Zion, Haste

ANGELIC SONGS. 11 10, 11 10. With Refrain.

Mary Ann Thomson, 1834-1923   James Walch, 1837-1901

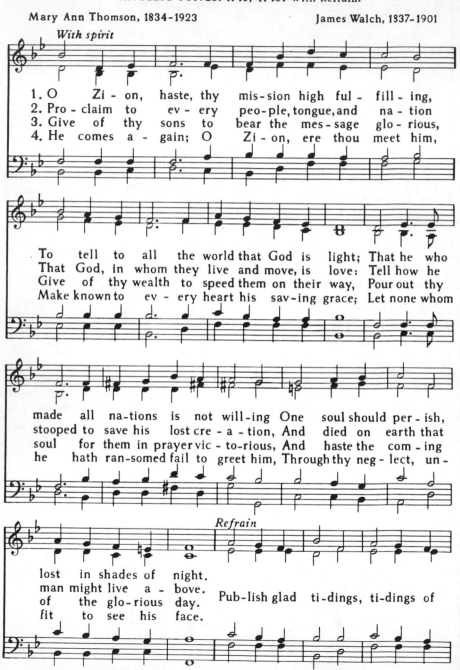

With spirit

1. O Zi - on, haste, thy mis-sion high ful - fill - ing,
2. Pro - claim to ev - ery peo-ple, tongue, and na - tion
3. Give of thy sons to bear the mes-sage glo - rious,
4. He comes a - gain; O Zi - on, ere thou meet him,

To tell to all the world that God is light; That he who
That God, in whom they live and move, is love: Tell how he
Give of thy wealth to speed them on their way, Pour out thy
Make known to ev - ery heart his sav-ing grace; Let none whom

made all na-tions is not will-ing One soul should per - ish,
stooped to save his lost cre - a - tion, And died on earth that
soul for them in prayer vic - to-rious, And haste the com - ing
he hath ran-somed fail to greet him, Through thy neg - lect, un-

lost in shades of night.
man might live a - bove.
of the glo - rious day.   Pub-lish glad ti-dings, ti-dings of
fit to see his face.

Refrain

peace;   Ti-dings of   Je - sus, re-demp-tion and re- lease.

Spread, O Spread, Thou Mighty Word   127
GOTT SEI DANK. 77, 77.

Jonathan F. Bahnmaier, 1774-1841   Freylinghausen's *Gesangbuch*, 1704
Tr. Catherine Winkworth, 1829-1878
Revised, *The Hymnal 1940*

With spirit

1. Spread,O spread,thou might-y Word,Spread the king-dom of the Lord,
2. Word of   how the Fa-ther's will Made the world,and keeps it, still;
3. Word of   how the Sav-ior's love Earth's sore bur-den doth re - move;
4. Might-y Word God's Spir-it gave, Man for heaven-ly life to save;
5. Word of   life, most pure and strong,Word for which the na-tions long,

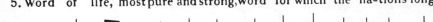

That   to   earth's re-mot-est bound Men   may heed the joy-ful   sound;
How   his   on - ly Son he gave, Man   from sin and death to   save;
How   for   ev - er in its need, Through his death the world is   freed;
Word through whose all-ho-ly might Man   can will and do the   right;
Spread a - broad,un-til from night All   the world a-wakes to   light.

Translation by permission of The Church Pension Fund.

128   ## Remember All the People

FAR OFF LANDS. 76, 76. D.

Percy Dearmer, 1867-1936

Moravian Melody

1. Re-mem-ber all the peo-ple Who live in far-off lands,
2. God bless the men and wom-en Who serve him o-ver-seas;

In strange and love-ly cit-ies, Or roam the des-ert sands,
God raise up more to help them To set the na-tions free,

Or farm the moun-tain pas-tures, Or till the end-less plains
Till all the dis-tant peo-ple In ev-ery for-eign place

Where chil-dren wade through rice-fields, And watch the cam-el-trains.
Shall un-der-stand his king-dom And come in-to his grace. A-men.

Jesus Shall Reign Where'er the Sun　129
DUKE STREET. L. M.

Isaac Watts, 1674-1748　　　　　　　　　John Hatton, d. 1793

With breadth

1. Je - sus shall reign wher - e'er the sun
2. To him shall end - less prayer be made,
3. Peo - ple and realms of ev - ery tongue
4. Bless - ings a - bound wher - e'er he reigns;
5. Let ev - ery crea - ture rise and bring

Doth his suc - ces - sive jour - neys run;
And prais - es throng to crown his head;
Dwell on his love with sweet - est song;
The pris - oner leaps to lose his chains,
Pe - cu - liar hon - ors to our King;

His king - dom stretch from shore to shore,
His Name like sweet per - fume shall rise
And in - fant voic - es shall pro - claim
The wea - ry find e - ter - nal rest,
An - gels de - scend with songs a - gain,

Till moons shall wax and wane no more.
With ev - ery morn - ing sac - ri - fice.
Their ear - ly bless - ings on his Name.
And all the sons of want are blest.
And earth re - peat the loud A - men.

130 O That the Lord Would Guide My Ways

EVAN. C. M.

Isaac Watts, 1674-1748

William H. Havergal, 1793-1870

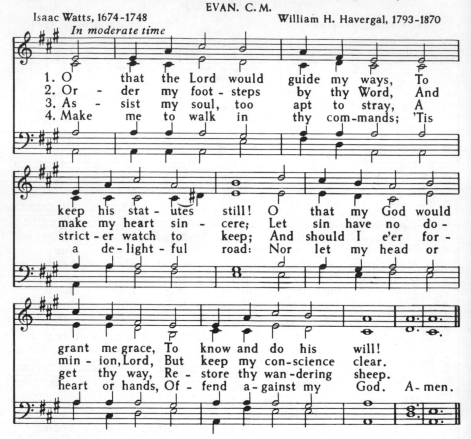

In moderate time

1. O that the Lord would guide my ways, To keep his stat-utes still! O that my God would grant me grace, To know and do his will!
2. Or - der my foot - steps by thy Word, And make my heart sin - cere; Let sin have no do - min - ion, Lord, But keep my con-science clear.
3. As - sist my soul, too apt to stray, A strict - er watch to keep; And should I e'er for - get thy way, Re - store thy wan - dering sheep.
4. Make me to walk in thy com-mands; 'Tis a de - light - ful road: Nor let my head or heart or hands, Of - fend a - gainst my God. A - men.

God the Father is often represented by a hand pointing downward out of a cloud. This suggests the hand of the Creator, and also the idea that the hand of God is over the souls of the righteous. The cloud is used to show that the full sight of God's majesty would be too much for human eyes.

O God, Accept My Heart This Day 131

ST. PETER. C. M.

Matthew Bridges, 1800-1894   Alexander R. Reinagle, 1799-1877

In moderate time

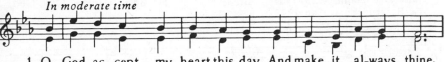

1. O God, ac-cept my heart this day, And make it al-ways thine,
2. Be-fore the Cross of him who died, Be-hold, I pros-trate fall;
3. A-noint me with thy heaven-ly grace, And seal me for thine own,
4. Let ev-ery thought and work and word To thee be ev-er given;

That I from thee no more may stray, No more from thee de-cline.
Let ev-ery sin be cru-ci-fied, And Christ be all in all.
That I may see thy glo-rious face, And wor-ship at thy throne.
Then life shall be thy ser-vice, Lord, And death the gate of heaven. Amen.

Savior, Teach Me, Day by Day 132

Jane E. Leeson, 1807-1882   FERRIER. 77, 77.   John B. Dykes, 1823-1876

In moderate time

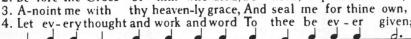

1. Sav-ior, teach me, day by day, Love's sweet les-son to o-bey;
2. With a child's glad heart of love At thy bid-ding may I move,
3. Teach me thus thy steps to trace, Strong to fol-low in thy grace,
4. Love in lov-ing finds em-ploy In o-be-dience all her joy;
5. Thus may I re-joice to show That I feel the love I owe;

Sweet-er les-son can-not be, Lov-ing him who first loved me.
Prompt to serve and fol-low thee, Lov-ing him who first loved me.
Learn-ing how to love from thee, Lov-ing him who first loved me.
Ev-er new that joy will be, Lov-ing him who first loved me.
Sing-ing till thy face I see, Of his love who first loved me.

133 O Take My Hand, Dear Father

SO NIMM DENN MEINE HÄNDE. 74, 74. D.

Julia Hausmann, 1825-1901
Tr. H. Brueckner, 1866-1942

Friedrich Silcher, 1789-1860

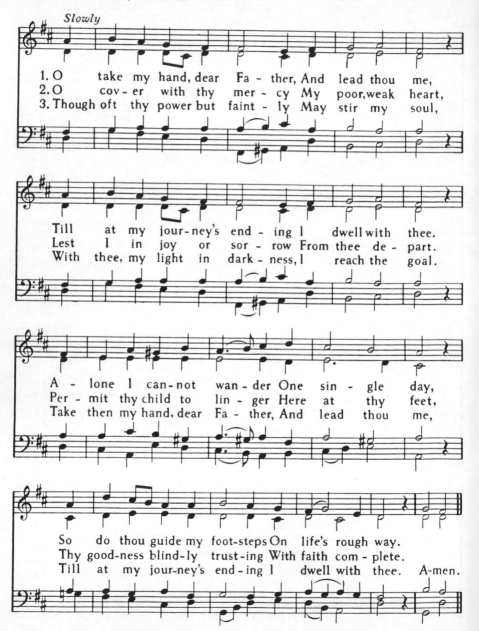

1. O take my hand, dear Fa - ther, And lead thou me,
2. O cov - er with thy mer - cy My poor, weak heart,
3. Though oft thy power but faint - ly May stir my soul,

Till at my jour-ney's end - ing I dwell with thee.
Lest I in joy or sor - row From thee de - part.
With thee, my light in dark - ness, I reach the goal.

A - lone I can - not wan - der One sin - gle day,
Per - mit thy child to lin - ger Here at thy feet,
Take then my hand, dear Fa - ther, And lead thou me,

So do thou guide my foot-steps On life's rough way.
Thy good-ness blind-ly trust-ing With faith com - plete.
Till at my jour-ney's end-ing I dwell with thee. A-men.

FAITH AND TRUST
My Faith Looks Up to Thee
OLIVET. 664, 6664.

Ray Palmer, 1808-1887

Lowell Mason, 1792-1872

With movement

1. My faith looks up to thee, Thou Lamb of Cal - va - ry, Sav - ior di - vine! Now hear me while I pray, Take all my guilt a - way, O let me from this day Be whol - ly thine.

2. May thy rich grace im - part Strength to my faint - ing heart, My zeal in - spire; As thou hast died for me, O may my love to thee, Pure, warm, and change-less be, A liv - ing fire.

3. While life's dark maze I tread, And griefs a - round me spread, Be thou my guide; Bid dark - ness turn to day, Wipe sor - row's tears a - way, Nor let me ev - er stray From thee a - side.

4. When ends life's tran - sient dream, When death's cold sul - len stream Shall o'er me roll; Blest Sav - ior, then, in love, Fear and dis - trust re - move; O bear me safe a - bove, A ran-somed soul. A-men.

135 Faith of Our Fathers

ST. CATHERINE. 88, 88, 88.

Frederick W. Faber, 1814-1863

Henri F. Hemy, 1818-1888
Adapt. James G. Walton, 1821-1905

Broadly

1. Faith of our fa - thers, liv - ing still In spite of
2. Our fa-thers, chained in pris - ons dark, Were still in
3. Faith of our fa - thers, we will love Both friend and

dun-geon, fire, and sword; O how our hearts beat high with
heart and con-science free, And blest would be their chil- dren's
foe in all our strife; And preach thee, too, as love knows

Refrain

joy When-e'er we hear that glo - rious word:
fate, If they, like them, should die for thee: Faith of our
how, By kind - ly words and vir - tuous life:

fa-thers, ho - ly faith, We will be true to thee till death.

Rock of Ages

TOPLADY. 77, 77, 77.

Augustus M. Toplady, 1740-1778

Thomas Hastings, 1784-1872

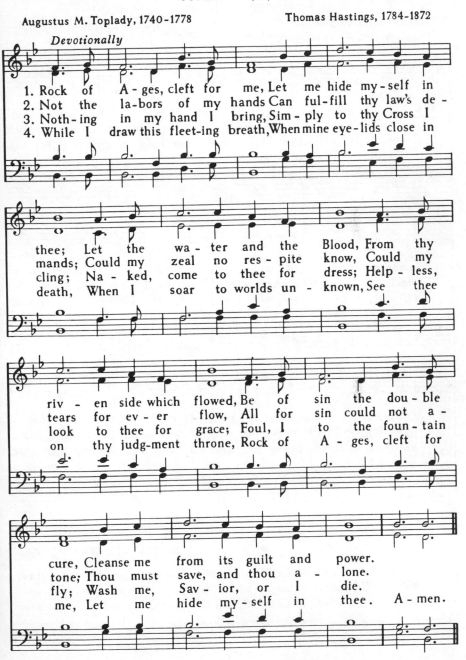

1. Rock of A - ges, cleft for me, Let me hide my - self in thee; Let the wa - ter and the Blood, From thy riv - en side which flowed, Be of sin the dou - ble cure, Cleanse me from its guilt and power.

2. Not the la - bors of my hands Can ful - fill thy law's de - mands; Could my zeal no res - pite know, Could my tears for ev - er flow, All for sin could not a - tone; Thou must save, and thou a - lone.

3. Noth - ing in my hand I bring, Sim - ply to thy Cross I cling; Na - ked, come to thee for dress; Help - less, look to thee for grace; Foul, I to the foun - tain fly; Wash me, Sav - ior, or I die.

4. While I draw this fleet - ing breath, When mine eye - lids close in death, When I soar to worlds un - known, See thee on thy judg - ment throne, Rock of A - ges, cleft for me, Let me hide my - self in thee. A - men.

137 Jesus, Priceless Treasure

JESU, MEINE FREUDE. 665, 665, 786.

FIRST TUNE

Johann Franck, 1618-1677
Tr. Catherine Winkworth, 1829-1878

Johann Crüger, 1598-1662

Broadly

1. Je - sus, price-less Treas-ure, Source of pur - est pleas-ure, Tru-est
2. In thine arm I rest me; Foes who would mo-lest me Can-not
3. Hence, all thoughts of sad - ness! For the Lord of glad-ness, Je - sus,

Friend to me; Long my heart hath pant - ed, Till it well - nigh
reach me here. Though the earth be shak-ing, Ev - ery heart be
en - ters in; Those who love the Fa - ther, Though the storms may

faint - ed, Thirst-ing aft - er thee. Thine I am, O spot-less Lamb,
quak-ing, God dis-pels our fear; Sin and hell in con-flict fell
gath - er, Still have peace with-in; Yea, what-e'er we here must bear,

I will suf - fer nought to hide thee, Ask for nought be - side thee.
With their heav-iest storms as-sail us: Je - sus will not fail us.
Still in thee lies pur - est pleas - ure, Je - sus, price-less Treas-ure.

8

Jesus, Priceless Treasure

LINDEMAN. 665, 665, 786.

SECOND TUNE

Johann Franck, 1618-1677
Tr. Catherine Winkworth, 1829-1878

Ludvig M. Lindeman, 1812-1887

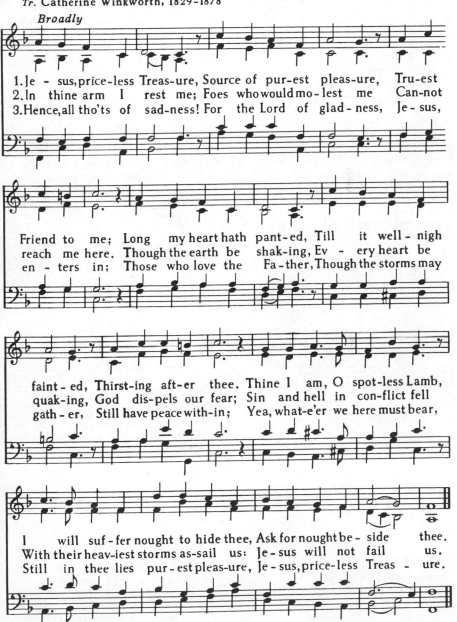

1. Je - sus, price-less Treas-ure, Source of pur-est pleas-ure, Tru-est
2. In thine arm I rest me; Foes who would mo-lest me Can-not
3. Hence, all tho'ts of sad-ness! For the Lord of glad-ness, Je-sus,

Friend to me; Long my heart hath pant-ed, Till it well-nigh
reach me here. Though the earth be shak-ing, Ev-ery heart be
en-ters in; Those who love the Fa-ther, Though the storms may

faint-ed, Thirst-ing aft-er thee. Thine I am, O spot-less Lamb,
quak-ing, God dis-pels our fear; Sin and hell in con-flict fell
gath-er, Still have peace with-in; Yea, what-e'er we here must bear,

I will suf-fer nought to hide thee, Ask for nought be - side thee.
With their heav-iest storms as-sail us: Je-sus will not fail us.
Still in thee lies pur-est pleas-ure, Je-sus, price-less Treas - ure.

Just As I Am

WOODWORTH. L. M.

Charlotte Elliott, 1789-1871   William B. Bradbury, 1816-1868

In moderate time

1. Just as I am, with-out one plea, But
2. Just as I am, and wait-ing not, To
3. Just as I am, though tossed a-bout With
4. Just as I am, poor, wretch-ed, blind; Sight,

that thy Blood was shed for me, And that thou bidd'st me
rid my soul of one dark blot, To thee, whose Blood can
many a con-flict, many a doubt, Fight-ings and fears with-
rich-es, heal-ing of the mind, Yea, all I need, in

come to thee, O Lamb of God, I come, I come.
cleanse each spot, O Lamb of God, I come, I come.
in, with-out, O Lamb of God, I come, I come.
thee to find, O Lamb of God, I come, I come.

5. Just as I am, thou wilt receive,
Wilt welcome, pardon, cleanse, relieve;
Because thy promise I believe,
O Lamb of God, I come.

6. Just as I am; thy love unknown
Has broken every barrier down;
Now to be thine, yea thine alone,
O Lamb of God, I come.

139   I Need Thee, Precious Jesus
Tune: PASSION CHORALE (No. 50)
or ST. CHRISTOPHER (No. 49)

I need thee, precious Jesus,
For I am full of sin;
My soul is dark and guilty,
My heart is dead within;

I need the cleansing fountain
Where I can always flee,
The Blood of Christ most precious,
The sinner's perfect plea.

Frederick Whitfield, 1829-1904

The Lord's My Shepherd

BROTHER JAMES' AIR. 86, 86, 86.

Based on Psalm 23

James L. M. Bain, 184?-1925
Adapt. from Gordon Jacob, 1934
by Walter W. Felton, 1955

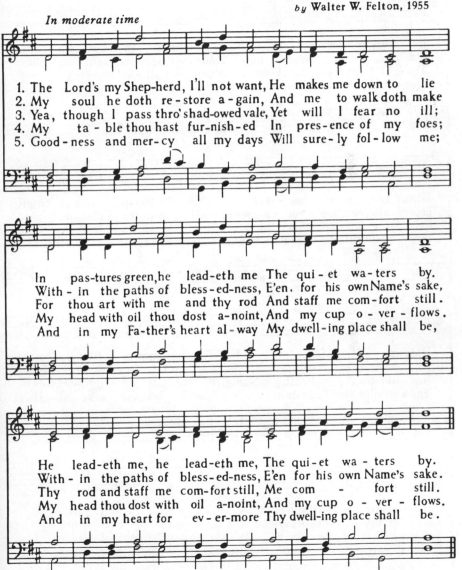

1. The Lord's my Shep-herd, I'll not want, He makes me down to lie
2. My soul he doth re-store a-gain, And me to walk doth make
3. Yea, though I pass thro' shad-owed vale, Yet will I fear no ill;
4. My ta-ble thou hast fur-nish-ed In pres-ence of my foes;
5. Good-ness and mer-cy all my days Will sure-ly fol-low me;

In pas-tures green, he lead-eth me The qui-et wa-ters by.
With-in the paths of bless-ed-ness, E'en for his own Name's sake,
For thou art with me and thy rod And staff me com-fort still.
My head with oil thou dost a-noint, And my cup o-ver-flows.
And in my Fa-ther's heart al-way My dwell-ing place shall be,

He lead-eth me, he lead-eth me, The qui-et wa-ters by.
With-in the paths of bless-ed-ness, E'en for his own Name's sake.
Thy rod and staff me com-fort still, Me com - fort still.
My head thou dost with oil a-noint, And my cup o-ver-flows.
And in my heart for ev-er-more Thy dwell-ing place shall be.

141 ### Jesus, Lover of My Soul

MARTYN. 77, 77. D.

Charles Wesley, 1707-1788

Simeon B. Marsh, 1798-1875

Devotionally

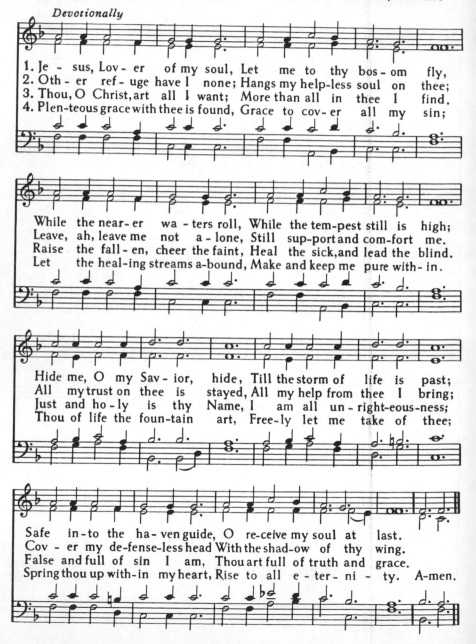

1. Je - sus, Lov - er of my soul, Let me to thy bos - om fly,
2. Oth - er ref - uge have I none; Hangs my help-less soul on thee;
3. Thou, O Christ, art all I want; More than all in thee I find.
4. Plen-teous grace with thee is found, Grace to cov-er all my sin;

While the near - er wa - ters roll, While the tem-pest still is high;
Leave, ah, leave me not a - lone, Still sup-port and com-fort me.
Raise the fall - en, cheer the faint, Heal the sick, and lead the blind.
Let the heal-ing streams a-bound, Make and keep me pure with - in.

Hide me, O my Sav - ior, hide, Till the storm of life is past;
All my trust on thee is stayed, All my help from thee I bring;
Just and ho - ly is thy Name, I am all un - right-eous-ness;
Thou of life the foun-tain art, Free-ly let me take of thee;

Safe in - to the ha - ven guide, O re-ceive my soul at last.
Cov - er my de-fense-less head With the shad-ow of thy wing.
False and full of sin I am, Thou art full of truth and grace.
Spring thou up with-in my heart, Rise to all e - ter - ni - ty. A-men.

The King of Love My Shepherd Is   142

ST. COLUMBA. 87, 87.

Henry W. Baker, 1821-1877
Based on Psalm 23

Traditional Irish Hymn Melody

Tenderly, in moderate time

1. The King of Love my Shep-herd is, Whose good-ness fail-eth nev-er; I noth-ing lack if I am his, And he is mine for ev-er.
2. Where streams of liv-ing wa-ter flow My ran-somed soul he lead-eth, And where the ver-dant pas-tures grow With food ce-les-tial feed-eth.
3. Per-verse and fool-ish oft I strayed, But yet in love he sought me, And on his shoul-der gent-ly laid, And home, re-joic-ing, brought me.
4. In death's dark vale I fear no ill With thee, dear Lord, be-side me; Thy rod and staff my com-fort still, Thy Cross be-fore to guide me. A-men.

5. Thou spread'st a table in my sight;
Thy unction grace bestoweth;
And O what transport and delight
From thy pure chalice floweth!

6. And so through all the length of days
Thy goodness faileth never;
Good Shepherd, may I sing thy praise
Within thy house for ever.

143 This Is My Father's World

TERRA PATRIS. S. M. D.

Maltbie D. Babcock, 1858-1901   Franklin L. Sheppard, 1852-1930

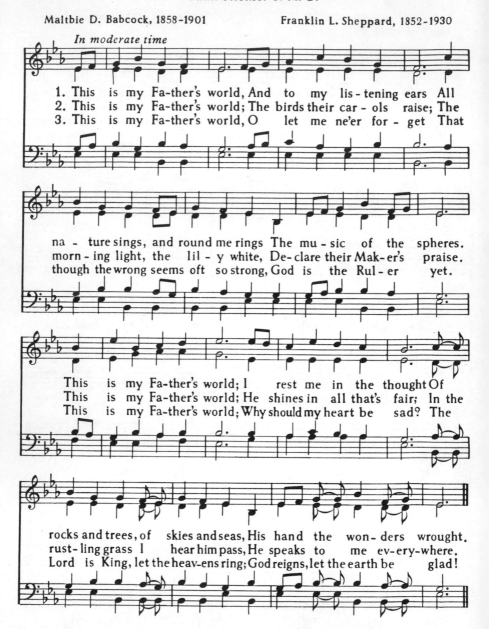

In moderate time

1. This is my Fa-ther's world, And to my lis-tening ears All
2. This is my Fa-ther's world; The birds their car-ols raise; The
3. This is my Fa-ther's world, O let me ne'er for-get That

na - ture sings, and round me rings The mu - sic of the spheres.
morn - ing light, the lil - y white, De-clare their Mak-er's praise.
though the wrong seems oft so strong, God is the Rul-er yet.

This is my Fa-ther's world; I rest me in the thought Of
This is my Fa-ther's world; He shines in all that's fair; In the
This is my Fa-ther's world; Why should my heart be sad? The

rocks and trees, of skies and seas, His hand the won-ders wrought.
rust-ling grass I hear him pass, He speaks to me ev-ery-where.
Lord is King, let the heav-ens ring; God reigns, let the earth be glad!

Savior, Like a Shepherd Lead Us

144

BRADBURY. 87, 87. D.

Dorothy A. Thrupp, 1779-1847 — William B. Bradbury, 1816-1868

1. Sav - ior, like a shep-herd lead us, Much we need thy ten - der care;
2. We are thine; do thou be-friend us, Be the guard-ian of our way;
3. Thou hast prom-ised to re - ceive us, Poor and sin - ful though we be;
4. Ear - ly let us seek thy fa - vor, Ear - ly let us do thy will;

In thy pleas-ant pas-tures feed us, For our use thy folds pre-pare:
Keep thy flock, from sin de - fend us, Seek us when we go a - stray:
Thou hast mer-cy to re - lieve us, Grace to cleanse, and power to free:
Bless - ed Lord and on - ly Sav-ior, With thy love our bos-oms fill:

Bless-ed Je-sus, Bless-ed Je-sus, Thou hast bought us: thine we are;
Bless-ed Je-sus, Bless-ed Je-sus, Hear us chil-dren when we pray;
Bless-ed Je-sus, Bless-ed Je-sus, Ear - ly let us turn to thee;
Bless-ed Je-sus, Bless-ed Je-sus, Thou hast loved us, love us still;

Bless-ed Je-sus, Bless-ed Je-sus, Thou hast bought us: thine we are.
Bless-ed Je-sus, Bless-ed Je-sus, Hear us chil-dren when we pray.
Bless-ed Je-sus, Bless-ed Je-sus, Ear - ly let us turn to thee.
Bless-ed Je-sus, Bless-ed Je-sus, Thou hast loved us, love us still. A-men.

145 Loving Shepherd of Thy Sheep

INNOCENTS. 77, 77.

Jane E. Leeson, 1807-1882 — *The Parish Choir,* London, 1850

In moderate time

1. Lov - ing Shep-herd of thy sheep, Keep thy lamb, in safe-ty keep;
2. Lov - ing Sav- ior, thou didst give Thine own life that we might live;
3. I would bless thee ev - ery day, Glad-ly all thy will o - bey,
4. Lov - ing Shep-herd, ev - er near, Teach thy lamb thy voice to hear;
5. Where thou lead-est I would go Walk-ing in thy steps be - low,

Noth-ing can thy power with-stand, None can pluck me from thy hand.
And the hands out-stretched to bless Bear the cru - el nails' im-press.
Like thy bless-ed ones a-bove, Hap-py in thy pre-cious love.
Suf - fer not my steps to stray From the straight and nar-row way.
Till be - fore my Fa - ther's throne I shall know as I am known. Amen.

146 Children of the Heavenly Father

SANDELL (TRYGGARE KAN INGEN VARA). L. M.

Caroline V. Sandell Berg, 1832-1903 — Swedish Melody
Tr. Ernst W. Olson, 1870-1958

Simply

1. Chil-dren of the heaven-ly Fa-ther Safe-ly in his bos- om gath-er;
2. God his own doth tend and nour-ish, In his ho-ly courts they flour-ish.
3. Nei - ther life nor death shall ev - er From the Lord his chil-dren sev - er;
4. Though he giv - eth or he tak-eth, God his chil-dren ne'er for - sak-eth,

Nest-ling bird nor star in heav - en Such a ref - uge e'er was giv - en.
From all e - vil things he spares them, In his might-y arms he bears them.
Un - to them his grace he show-eth, And their sor-rows all he know-eth.
His the lov-ing pur-pose sole - ly To pre-serve them pure and ho - ly.

In Heavenly Love Abiding

HEAVENLY LOVE. 76, 76. D.

Anna L. Waring, 1820-1910

Felix Mendelssohn, 1809-1847

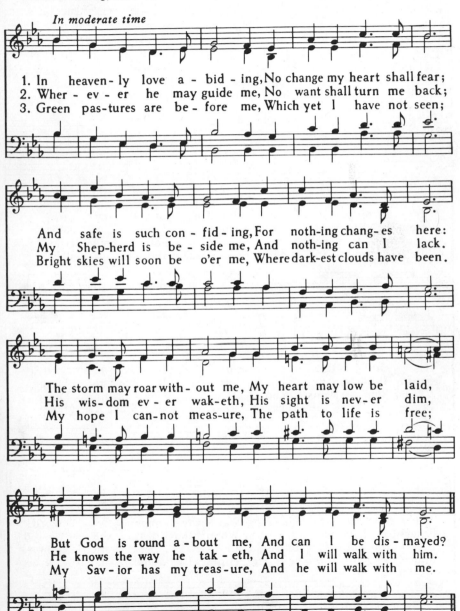

In moderate time

1. In heaven-ly love a-bid-ing, No change my heart shall fear;
2. Wher-ev-er he may guide me, No want shall turn me back;
3. Green pas-tures are be-fore me, Which yet I have not seen;

And safe is such con-fid-ing, For noth-ing chang-es here:
My Shep-herd is be-side me, And noth-ing can I lack.
Bright skies will soon be o'er me, Where dark-est clouds have been.

The storm may roar with-out me, My heart may low be laid,
His wis-dom ev-er wak-eth, His sight is nev-er dim,
My hope I can-not meas-ure, The path to life is free;

But God is round a-bout me, And can I be dis-mayed?
He knows the way he tak-eth, And I will walk with him.
My Sav-ior has my treas-ure, And he will walk with me.

148
At the Name of Jesus
KING'S WESTON. 65, 65. D.

Caroline M. Noel, 1817-1877,
and others

Ralph Vaughan Williams, 1872-1958

With vigor

1. At the Name of Je - sus Ev - ery knee shall bow,
2. Hum-bled for a sea - son, To re - ceive a name
3. In your hearts en - throne him; There let him sub - due
4. Glo - ry then to Je - sus, Who, the Prince of Light,

Ev - ery tongue con - fess him King of Glo - ry now;
From the lips of sin - ners Un - to whom he came,
All that is not ho - ly, All that is not true:
To a world in dark - ness Brought the gift of sight;

'Tis the Fa - ther's pleas - ure We should call him Lord,
Faith - ful - ly he bore it Spot - less to the last,
Crown him as your cap - tain In temp - ta - tion's hour;
Praise to God the Fa - ther; In the Spir - it's love

Who from the be - gin - ning Was the might - y Word.
Brought it back vic - to - rious When through death he passed.
Let his will en - fold you In its light and power.
Praise we all to - geth - er Him who reigns a - bove.

Music from SONGS OF PRAISE *by permission of Oxford University Press.*

Crown Him with Many Crowns

DIADEMATA. S. M. D.

Matthew Bridges, 1800-1894
Godfrey Thring, 1823-1903

George J. Elvey, 1816-1893

With dignity

1. Crown him with man-y crowns, The Lamb up-on his throne;
2. Crown him the Lord of Life, Who tri-umphed o'er the grave,
3. Crown him the Lord of Love, Be-hold his hands and side,
4. Crown him the Lord of Peace, Whose power a scep-ter sways
5. Crown him the Lord of Years, The Po-ten-tate of time,

Hark, how the heaven-ly an-them drowns All mu-sic but its own!
And rose vic-to-rious in the strife For those he came to save.
Rich wounds yet vis-i-ble a-bove In beau-ty glo-ri-fied.
From pole to pole, that wars may cease, Ab-sorbed in prayer and praise.
Cre-a-tor of the roll-ing spheres, In-ef-fa-bly sub-lime.

A-wake, my soul, and sing Of him who died for thee,
His glo-ries now we sing, Who died and rose on high,
No an-gel in the sky Can ful-ly bear that sight,
His reign shall know no end, And round his pierc-ed feet
All hail, Re-deem-er, hail! For thou hast died for me;

And hail him as thy match-less King Through all e-ter-ni-ty.
Who died, e-ter-nal life to bring, And lives that death may die.
But down-ward bends his burn-ing eye At mys-ter-ies so bright.
Fair flowers of Par-a-dise ex-tend Their fra-grance ev-er sweet.
Thy praise and glo-ry shall not fail Through-out e-ter-ni-ty.

150   That Sweet Story of Old

SWEET STORY (LUKE). Irregular.

Jemima Luke, 1813-1906

Greek Melody,
Arr. William B. Bradbury, 1816-1868
Harm. Winfred Douglas, 1867-1944

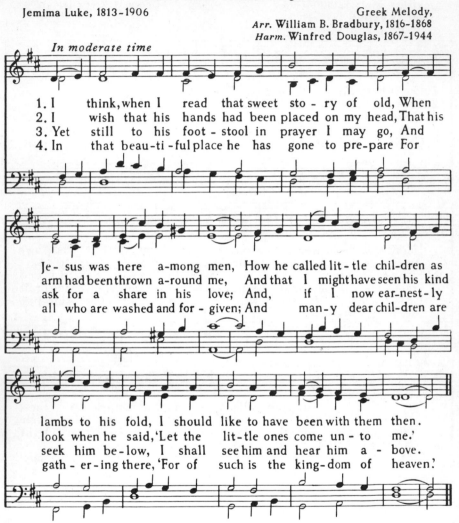

In moderate time

1. I think, when I read that sweet sto - ry of old, When
2. I wish that his hands had been placed on my head, That his
3. Yet still to his foot - stool in prayer I may go, And
4. In that beau - ti -ful place he has gone to pre-pare For

Je - sus was here a-mong men, How he called lit - tle chil-dren as
arm had been thrown a-round me, And that I might have seen his kind
ask for a share in his love; And, if I now ear-nest-ly
all who are washed and for - given; And man-y dear chil-dren are

lambs to his fold, I should like to have been with them then.
look when he said, 'Let the lit-tle ones come un - to me.'
seek him be-low, I shall see him and hear him a - bove.
gath - er-ing there, 'For of such is the king-dom of heaven.'

5. But thousands and thousands, who wander and fall,
   Never heard of that heavenly home;
   I should like them to know there is room for them all,
   And that Jesus has bid them to come.

6. I long for the joy of that glorious time,
   The sweetest and brightest and best,
   When the dear little children of every clime
   Shall crowd to his arms and be blest.

O Jesu So Meek, O Jesu So Kind 151

O JESULEIN SÜSS. Irregular.

Valentin Thilo, 1607–1662
Cologne, 1623
Tr. Geoffrey W. Daisley, 1877–1939
Figured bass, J. S. Bach, 1685–1750

1. O Je-su so meek, O Je-su so kind, Thou hast ful-filled thy Fa-ther's mind; Hast come from heav-en down to earth In hu-man flesh through hu-man birth. O Je-su so meek, O Je-su so kind!

2. O Je-su so good, O Je-su so meek, To do thy will is all we seek; For all we are or have is thine; Do thou our hearts to thee in-cline. O Je-su so good, O Je-su so meek!

152 O Sing, All Ye Lands

HOFF. 11 5, 12 9.

Ulrik V. Koren, 1826-1910
Tr. Harriet R. K. Spaeth, 1845-1925, *alt.*
Based on Psalm 100

Erik C. Hoff, 1830-1894

Joyfully

1. O sing, all ye lands, with a ju-bi-lant voice;
2. The Lord, he is God, he hath made us, not we;
3. O en-ter his gates with thanks-giv-ing and praise;
4. For good is the Lord, and his mer-cy is sure;

Glo-ry be to God! O serve him with glad-ness, be-
Glo-ry be to God! The sheep of his pas-ture we
Glo-ry be to God! To hon-or his Name glad-some
Glo-ry be to God! To all gen-er-a-tions his

fore him now re-joice; Sing praise un-to God out of Zi-on!
ev-er-more shall be; Sing praise un-to God out of Zi-on!
voic-es we will raise; Sing praise un-to God out of Zi-on!
truth shall e'er en-dure; Sing praise un-to God out of Zi-on!

153 Let Us with a Gladsome Mind

MONKLAND. 77, 77.

John Milton, 1608-1674
Based on Psalm 136

Moravian Melody
Arr. John B. Wilkes, 1785-1869

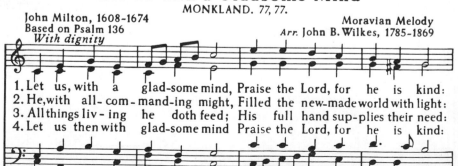

With dignity

1. Let us, with a glad-some mind, Praise the Lord, for he is kind:
2. He, with all-com-mand-ing might, Filled the new-made world with light:
3. All things liv-ing he doth feed; His full hand sup-plies their need:
4. Let us then with glad-some mind Praise the Lord, for he is kind:

Refrain

For his mer-cies shall en-dure, Ev - er faith-ful, ev-er sure.

This hymn may also be sung to GOTT SEI DANK *(No.127).*

Praise Ye the Father 154

FLEMMING (INTEGER VITAE). 11 11 11, 5.

Elizabeth R. Charles, 1828-1896   Friedrich F. Flemming, 1778-1813

In moderate time

1. Praise ye the Fa - ther for his lov-ing-kind-ness; Ten-der - ly
2. Praise ye the Sav - ior, great is his com-pas - sion; Gra-cious - ly
3. Praise ye the Spir - it, Com-fort-er of Is - rael, Sent of the

cares he for his err-ing chil-dren; Praise him, ye an - gels,
cares he for his cho-sen peo - ple; Young men and maid-ens,
Fa - ther and the Son to bless us, Praise ye the Fa - ther,

praise him in the heav-ens, Praise ye Je - ho - vah.
ye old men and chil - dren, Praise ye the Sav - ior.
Son, and Ho - ly Spir - it, Praise ye the Tri-une God.

155 Let the Whole Creation Cry

SALZBURG (ALLE MENSCHEN). 77, 77. D.

Stopford A. Brooke, 1832-1916

Jakob Hintze, 1622-1702
Harm. J. S. Bach, 1685-1750

With vigor

1. Let the whole cre - a - tion cry, 'Glo - ry to the Lord on high!'
2. War-riors fight-ing for the Lord, Proph-ets burn-ing with his word,
3. Men and wom-en, young and old, Raise the an-them man - i - fold,

Heaven and earth, a - wake and sing, 'God is good and there-fore King!'
Those to whom the arts be - long, Add their voic-es to the song.
And let chil-dren's hap - py hearts In this wor-ship bear their parts;

Praise him, all ye hosts a - bove, Ev - er bright and fair in love;
Kings of know-ledge and of law, To the glo - rious cir - cle draw;
From the north to south-ern pole Let the might-y cho - rus roll:

Sun and moon, up-lift your voice, Night and stars, in God re - joice!
All who work and all who wait, Sing, 'The Lord is good and great!'
'Ho-ly, ho - ly, ho - ly One, Glo - ry be to God a - lone!'

O Savior, Precious Savior

ANGEL'S STORY. 76, 76. D.

Frances R. Havergal, 1836-1879

Arthur H. Mann, 1850-1929

In moderate time

1. O Sav-ior, pre-cious Sav-ior, Whom yet un-seen we love;
2. O bring-er of sal - va-tion, Who won-drous-ly hast wrought,
3. In thee all full-ness dwell-eth, All grace and power di - vine;
4. O grant the con-sum - ma-tion Of this our song a - bove,

O Name of might and fa - vor, All oth - er names a - bove;
Thy-self the rev - e - la-tion Of love be-yond our thought;
The glo - ry that ex - cel-leth, O Son of God, is thine.
In end - less ad - o - ra-tion And ev - er-last - ing love;

We wor - ship thee, we bless thee, To thee a - lone we sing;
We wor - ship thee, we bless thee, To thee a - lone we sing;
We wor - ship thee, we bless thee, To thee a - lone we sing;
Then shall we praise and bless thee Where per - fect prais-es ring,

We praise thee and con-fess thee, Our ho - ly Lord and King.
We praise thee and con-fess thee, Our gra-cious Lord and King.
We praise thee and con-fess thee, Our glo-rious Lord and King.
And ev - er-more con-fess thee, Our Sav-ior and our King. A-men.

157 Holy God, We Praise Thy Name

TE DEUM (GROSSER GOTT). 78, 78, 77.

German, XVIII *cent.*
Tr. Clarence A. Walworth, 1820-1900

Allgemeines Katholisches
Gesangbuch, Vienna, 1774

With dignity

1. Ho - ly God, we praise thy Name; Lord of all, we
2. Hark, the loud ce - les - tial hymn An - gel choirs a -
3. Lo, the Ap - os - tol - ic train Joins the sa - cred
4. Ho - ly Fa - ther, Ho - ly Son, Ho - ly Spir - it,

bow be - fore thee! All on earth thy scep - ter claim, All in
bove are rais - ing, Cher - u - bim and ser - a - phim, In un -
Name to hal - low; Proph - ets swell the loud re - frain, And the
Three we name thee; While in es - sence on - ly One, Un - di -

heaven a - bove a - dore thee; In - fi - nite thy vast do -
ceas - ing cho - rus prais - ing; Fill the heavens with sweet ac -
white-robed mar - tyrs fol - low; And from morn to set of
vid - ed God we claim thee; And a - dor - ing bend the

main, Ev - er - last - ing is thy reign.
cord: Ho - ly, ho - ly, ho - ly, Lord.
sun, Through the church the song goes on.
knee, While we own the mys - ter - y. A - men.

The God of Abraham Praise 158

LEONI (YIGDAL). 66, 84. D.

Thomas Olivers, 1725-1799
Based on the *Yigdal*

Traditional Hebrew Melody
XVII *cent.*

With spirit

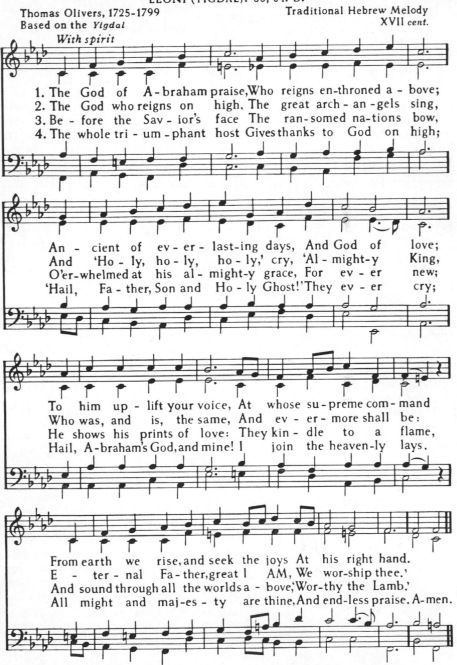

1. The God of A - braham praise, Who reigns en-throned a - bove;
2. The God who reigns on high, The great arch - an - gels sing,
3. Be - fore the Sav - ior's face The ran-somed na-tions bow,
4. The whole tri - um - phant host Gives thanks to God on high;

An - cient of ev - er - last-ing days, And God of love;
And 'Ho - ly, ho - ly, ho - ly,' cry, 'Al - might-y King,
O'er-whelmed at his al - might-y grace, For ev - er new;
'Hail, Fa - ther, Son and Ho - ly Ghost!' They ev - er cry;

To him up - lift your voice, At whose su - preme com - mand
Who was, and is, the same, And ev - er - more shall be:
He shows his prints of love: They kin - dle to a flame,
Hail, A-braham's God, and mine! I join the heaven-ly lays.

From earth we rise, and seek the joys At his right hand.
E - ter - nal Fa-ther, great I AM, We wor-ship thee.'
And sound through all the worlds a - bove, 'Wor-thy the Lamb.'
All might and maj-es - ty are thine, And end-less praise. A-men.

Our Life in Christ

PRAYER

159 Lord, Teach Us How to Pray Aright

EVAN. C. M.

James Montgomery, 1771-1854

William H. Havergal, 1793-1870

Quietly

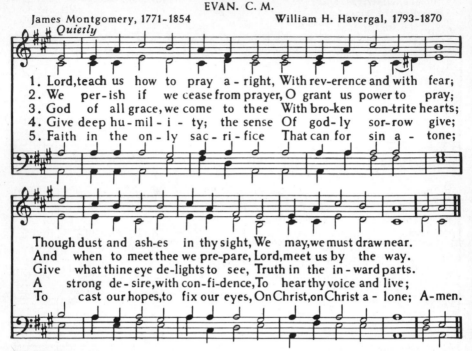

1. Lord, teach us how to pray a-right, With rev-erence and with fear;
2. We per-ish if we cease from prayer, O grant us power to pray;
3. God of all grace, we come to thee With bro-ken con-trite hearts;
4. Give deep hu-mil-i-ty; the sense Of god-ly sor-row give;
5. Faith in the on-ly sac-ri-fice That can for sin a-tone;

Though dust and ash-es in thy sight, We may, we must draw near.
And when to meet thee we pre-pare, Lord, meet us by the way.
Give what thine eye de-lights to see, Truth in the in-ward parts.
A strong de-sire, with con-fi-dence, To hear thy voice and live;
To cast our hopes, to fix our eyes, On Christ, on Christ a-lone; A-men.

6. Patience to watch and wait and weep,
Though mercy long delay;
Courage our fainting souls to keep,
And trust thee though thou slay.

7. Give these, and then thy will be done;
Thus strengthened with all might,
We, through thy Spirit and thy Son,
Shall pray, and pray aright.

The use of the descending dove as a symbol for God the Holy Spirit comes from the story of the baptism of Jesus: "And when Jesus was baptized, he went up immediately from the water, and behold, the heavens were opened and he saw the Spirit of God descending like a dove, and alighting on him; and lo, a voice from heaven, saying, 'This is my beloved Son, with whom I am well pleased'" (Matthew 3:16-17).

God Be in My Head

DAVID. Irregular.

Horae B.V. Mariae, 1514

George W. Briggs, 1875-1959

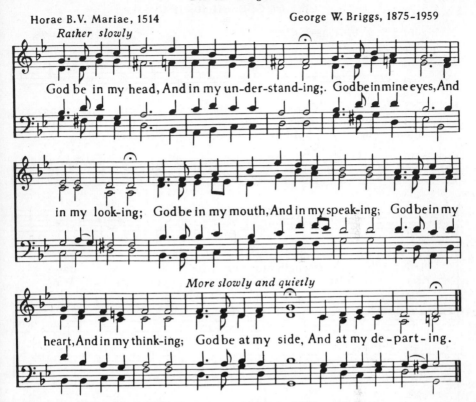

Rather slowly

God be in my head, And in my un-der-stand-ing;. God be in mine eyes, And in my look-ing; God be in my mouth, And in my speak-ing; God be in my heart, And in my think-ing; God be at my side, And at my de-part-ing.

More slowly and quietly

Music from SONGS OF PRAISE *by permission of Oxford University Press.*
The pronoun can be changed to "your" if sung for some one else, as at a Baptism or on a birthday.

This old English prayer, *God Be in My Head,* is very plain and simple, but it is a prayer with the biggest order in the world.

Each time we sing it we really do two things. First, we put ourselves and our own thoughts and desires to the side. Then we ask God to come and be the real Lord of our lives. Here we ask God to take charge, to rule and guide us in everything we think, say, and do.

This is a good prayer to make your own. Pray it every day. As you pray it, try to keep the door of your life open so God may answer your prayer— so he may come and be with you in your every thought, word, and deed.

161 O Jesus Christ, to Thee May Hymns Be Rising
CITY OF GOD. 11 10, 11 10.

Bradford G. Webster, 1898–

Daniel Moe, 1926–

With dignity

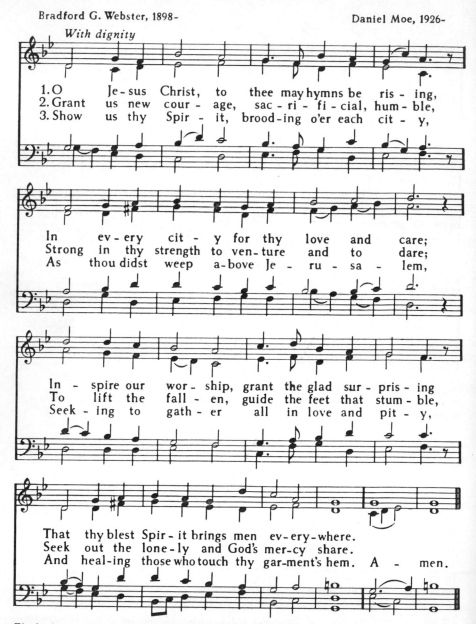

1. O Jesus Christ, to thee may hymns be ris - ing,
2. Grant us new cour - age, sac - ri - fi - cial, hum - ble,
3. Show us thy Spir - it, brood-ing o'er each cit - y,

In ev - ery cit - y for thy love and care;
Strong in thy strength to ven - ture and to dare;
As thou didst weep a - bove Je - ru - sa - lem,

In - spire our wor - ship, grant the glad sur - pris - ing
To lift the fall - en, guide the feet that stum - ble,
Seek - ing to gath - er all in love and pit - y,

That thy blest Spir - it brings men ev - ery-where.
Seek out the lone - ly and God's mer - cy share.
And heal - ing those who touch thy gar - ment's hem. A - men.

The hymn may be concluded by repeating the first stanza.

What a Friend We Have in Jesus

ERIE (WHAT A FRIEND). 87, 87. D.

Joseph Scriven, 1820-1886   Charles C. Converse, 1332-1918

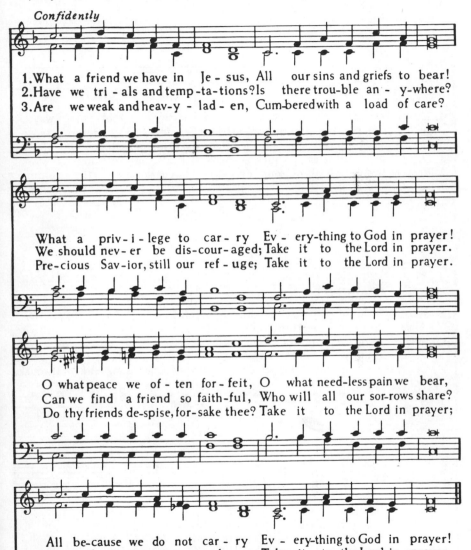

Confidently

1.What a friend we have in Je - sus, All our sins and griefs to bear!
2.Have we tri - als and temp-ta-tions? Is there trou-ble an - y-where?
3.Are we weak and heav-y - lad - en, Cum-bered with a load of care?

What a priv - i - lege to car - ry Ev - ery-thing to God in prayer!
We should nev - er be dis-cour-aged; Take it to the Lord in prayer.
Pre-cious Sav-ior, still our ref - uge; Take it to the Lord in prayer.

O what peace we of - ten for - feit, O what need-less pain we bear,
Can we find a friend so faith-ful, Who will all our sor-rows share?
Do thy friends de-spise, for-sake thee? Take it to the Lord in prayer;

All be-cause we do not car - ry Ev - ery-thing to God in prayer!
Je - sus knows our ev - ery weak-ness; Take it to the Lord in prayer.
In his arms he'll take and shield thee, Thou wilt find a sol-ace there.

163   Dear Lord and Father of Mankind

REST. 86, 886.

John Greenleaf Whittier, 1807-1892   Frederick C. Maker, 1844-1927

Quietly

1. Dear Lord and Fa-ther of man-kind, For-give our fool-ish ways;
2. In sim-ple trust like theirs who heard, Be-side the Syr-ian sea,
3. O Sab-bath rest by Gal-i-lee, O calm of hills a-bove;
4. Drop thy still dews of qui-et-ness, Till all our striv-ings cease;
5. Breathe thro' the heats of our de-sire Thy cool-ness and thy balm;

Re-clothe us in our right-ful mind, In pur-er lives thy
The gra-cious call-ing of the Lord, Let us, like them, with-
Where Je-sus knelt to share with thee The si-lence of e-
Take from our souls the strain and stress, And let our or-dered
Let sense be dumb, let flesh re-tire; Speak through the earth-quake,

serv-ice find, In deep-er rev-erence, praise.
out a word Rise up and fol-low thee.
ter-ni-ty, In-ter-pret-ed by love!
lives con-fess The beau-ty of thy peace.
wind, and fire, O still small voice of calm! A-men.

I Need Thee Every Hour

LOWRY. 64, 64. With Refrain.

Annie S. Hawks, 1835-1918
Refrain, Robert Lowry, 1826-1899

Robert Lowry, 1826-1899

In moderate time

1. I need thee ev-ery hour, Most gra - cious Lord;
2. I need thee ev-ery hour, Stay thou near by;
3. I need thee ev-ery hour, In joy or pain;
4. I need thee ev-ery hour, Teach me thy will;
5. I need thee ev-ery hour, Most Ho - ly One,

No ten-der voice like thine Can peace af - ford.
Temp - ta - tions lose their power When thou art nigh.
Come quick-ly and a - bide, Or life is vain.
And thy rich prom-is - es In me ful - fill.
O make me thine in - deed, Thou bless - ed Son.

Refrain

I need thee, O I need thee, Ev-ery hour I need thee;

O bless me now, my Sav-ior, I come to thee. A - men.

CONSECRATION

165
O Jesus, I Have Promised

MUNICH (MEININGEN). 76, 76. D.

John E. Bode, 1816-1874

Neuvermehrtes Gesangbuch, Meiningen, 1693
Adapt. and Harm. Felix Mendelssohn, 1809-1847

In moderate time

1. O Je-sus, I have prom-ised To serve thee to the end;
2. O let me feel thee near me, The world is ev-er near;
3. O let me hear thee speak-ing In ac-cents clear and still,
4. O Je-sus, thou hast prom-ised To all who fol-low thee,

Be thou for ev-er near me, My Mas-ter and my Friend;
I see the sights that daz-zle, The tempt-ing sounds I hear;
A-bove the storms of pas-sion, The mur-murs of self-will;
That where thou art in glo-ry There shall thy serv-ant be;

I shall not fear the bat-tle If thou art by my side,
My foes are ev-er near me, A-round me and with-in;
O speak to re-as-sure me, To has-ten or con-trol;
And, Je-sus, I have prom-ised To serve thee to the end;

Nor wan-der from the path-way If thou wilt be my guide.
But, Je-sus, draw thou near-er, And shield my soul from sin.
O speak, and make me lis-ten, Thou guard-ian of my soul.
O give me grace to fol-low, My Mas-ter and my Friend. A-men.

This hymn may also be sung to ANGEL'S STORY *(No. 156).*

Be Thou My Vision

SLANE. 10 10, 10 10.

Ancient Irish
Tr. Mary Byrne
Versified by Eleanor Hull

Ancient Irish Melody
Harm. David Evans

In moderate time

1. Be thou my Vis - ion, O Lord of my heart;
2. Be thou my Wis - dom, and thou my true Word,
3. Rich - es I heed not, nor man's emp - ty praise,
4. High King of Heav - en, my vic - to - ry won,

Naught be all else to me, save that thou art:
I ev - er with thee and thou with me, Lord:
Thou mine in - her - it - ance, now and al - ways:
May I reach heav - en's joys, O bright heav'n's Son!

Thou my best thought, by day or by night,
Thou my great Fa - ther, I thy true son;
Thou, and thou on - ly, first in my heart,
Heart of my own heart, what - ev - er be - fall,

Wak - ing or sleep - ing, thy pres - ence my light.
Thou in me dwell - ing, and I with thee one.
High King of Heav - en, my Treas - ure thou art.
Still be my Vis - ion, O Rul - er of all. A - men.

Words from POEM BOOK OF THE GAEL *published by Chatto and Windus, Ltd., London. Used by permission. Harmonization from* THE CHURCH HYMNARY, *Revised Edition. Used by permission of Oxford University Press.*

167 Jesus, Master, Whose I Am

ST. CHRYSOSTOM. 77, 77, 77.

Frances R. Havergal, 1836-1879   Jeremiah F. Ohl, 1850-1941

Devotionally

1. Je - sus, Mas - ter, whose I am, Pur - chased thine a -
2. Oth - er lords have long held sway; Now thy Name a -
3. Je - sus, Mas - ter, whom I serve, Though so fee - bly
4. Je - sus, Mas - ter, I am thine; Keep me faith - ful,

lone to be, By thy Blood, O spot - less Lamb,
lone to bear, Thy dear voice a - lone o - bey,
and so ill, Strength-en hand and heart and nerve
keep me near; Let thy pres - ence in me shine

Shed so will - ing - ly for me, Let my heart be
Is my dai - ly, hour-ly prayer; Whom have I in
All thy bid - ding to ful - fill; O - pen thou mine
All my home-ward way to cheer. Je - sus, at thy

all thine own, Let me live for thee a - lone.
heaven but thee? Noth-ing else my joy can be.
eyes to see All the work thou hast for me.
feet I fall, O be thou my all in all. A-men.

Let Me Be Thine for Ever

COPENHAGEN (JEG VIL MIG HERREN LOVE). 76, 76. D.

St. 1, Nikolaus Selnecker, 1532-1592

St. 2-3, Rudolstadt Gesangbuch, 1688

Tr. Matthias Loy, 1828-1915, alt.

Hartnack O. K. Zinck, 1746-1833

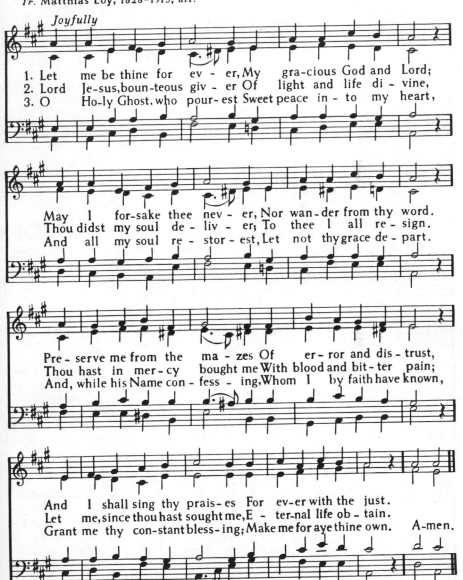

Joyfully

1. Let me be thine for ev - er, My gra-cious God and Lord;
2. Lord Je-sus, boun-teous giv - er Of light and life di - vine,
3. O Ho-ly Ghost, who pour-est Sweet peace in - to my heart,

May I for-sake thee nev - er, Nor wan-der from thy word.
Thou didst my soul de - liv - er; To thee I all re - sign.
And all my soul re - stor - est, Let not thy grace de - part.

Pre - serve me from the ma - zes Of er - ror and dis - trust,
Thou hast in mer - cy bought me With blood and bit - ter pain;
And, while his Name con - fess - ing, Whom I by faith have known,

And I shall sing thy prais - es For ev-er with the just.
Let me, since thou hast sought me, E - ter-nal life ob - tain.
Grant me thy con-stant bless - ing; Make me for aye thine own. A-men.

169 My Jesus, I Love Thee

GORDON. 11 11, 11 11.

William R. Featherstone, 1842-1878
The London Hymn Book, 1864

Adoniram J. Gordon, 1836-1895

Flowing

1. My Je - sus, I love thee, I know thou art mine,
2. I love thee be - cause thou hast first lov - ed me,
3. In man - sions of glo - ry and end - less de - light,

For thee all the fol - lies of sin I re - sign;
And pur-chased my par - don on Cal - va - ry's tree;
I'll ev - er a - dore thee in heav - en so bright;

My gra - cious Re - deem - er, my Sav - ior art thou;
I love thee for wear - ing the thorns on thy brow;
I'll sing with the glit - ter - ing crown on my brow;

If ev - er I loved thee, Lord Je - sus, 'tis now.
If ev - er I loved thee, Lord Je - sus, 'tis now.
If ev - er I loved thee, Lord Je - sus, 'tis now.

Thee Will I Love

ICH WILL DICH LIEBEN. 88, 88, 88.

Johann Scheffler, 1624-1677
Tr. John Wesley, 1703-1791

Harmonischer Liederschatz, Frankfurt, 1738

With spirit

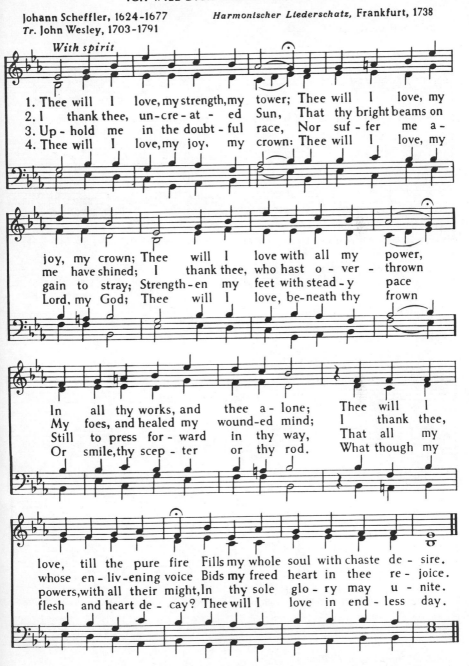

1. Thee will I love, my strength, my tower; Thee will I love, my
2. I thank thee, un-cre-at-ed Sun, That thy bright beams on
3. Up-hold me in the doubt-ful race, Nor suf-fer me a-
4. Thee will I love, my joy, my crown: Thee will I love, my

joy, my crown; Thee will I love with all my power,
me have shined; I thank thee, who hast o-ver-thrown
gain to stray; Strength-en my feet with stead-y pace
Lord, my God; Thee will I love, be-neath thy frown

In all thy works, and thee a-lone; Thee will I
My foes, and healed my wound-ed mind; I thank thee,
Still to press for-ward in thy way, That all my
Or smile, thy scep-ter or thy rod. What though my

love, till the pure fire Fills my whole soul with chaste de-sire.
whose en-liv-ening voice Bids my freed heart in thee re-joice.
powers, with all their might, In thy sole glo-ry may u-nite.
flesh and heart de-cay? Thee will I love in end-less day.

171   Christ Be with Me

KIROA. Irregular.

VIII *cent.* or later   Leland B. Sateren, 1913-
Tr. Cecil F. Alexander, 1823–1895, *alt.*

Christ be with me, Christ be-fore me, Christ be-hind me, Christ in me,

Christ be-neath me, Christ a-bove me, Christ on my right, Christ on my left,

Christ in the heart of ev - ery man who thinks of me,

Christ in the mouth of ev - ery - one who speaks of me,

Christ in ev-ery eye that sees me, Christ in ev-ery ear that hears me.

The Wise May Bring Their Learning

CHRISTMAS MORN. 76, 76. D.

172

Book of Praise for Children, 1881

Edward J. Hopkins, 1818-1901

In moderate time

1. The wise may bring their learn-ing, The rich may bring their wealth,
2. We'll bring him hearts that love him; We'll bring him thank-ful praise,
3. We'll bring the lit - tle du - ties We have to do each day;

And some may bring their great-ness, And some bring strength and health;
And young souls meek-ly striv-ing To walk in ho - ly ways;
We'll try our best to please him, At home, at school, at play;

We, too, would bring our treas-ures To of - fer to the King;
And these shall be the treas-ures We of - fer to the King,
And bet - ter are these treas-ures To of - fer to our King,

We have no wealth or learn-ing: What shall we chil-dren bring?
And these are gifts that e - ven The poor-est child may bring.
Than rich-est gifts with - out them; Yet these a child may bring.

173   Thy Life Was Given for Me

ST. OLAVE. 66, 66, 66.

Frances R. Havergal, 1836-1879   Joseph Barnby, 1838-1896

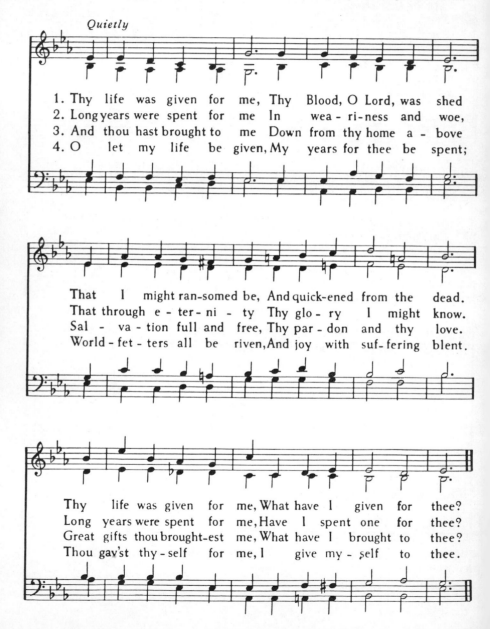

Quietly

1. Thy life was given for me, Thy Blood, O Lord, was shed
2. Long years were spent for me In wea-ri-ness and woe,
3. And thou hast brought to me Down from thy home a-bove
4. O let my life be given, My years for thee be spent;

That I might ran-somed be, And quick-ened from the dead.
That through e-ter-ni-ty Thy glo-ry I might know.
Sal-va-tion full and free, Thy par-don and thy love.
World-fet-ters all be riven, And joy with suf-fering blent.

Thy life was given for me, What have I given for thee?
Long years were spent for me, Have I spent one for thee?
Great gifts thou brought-est me, What have I brought to thee?
Thou gav'st thy-self for me, I give my-self to thee.

Take My Life, and Let It Be Consecrated   174

PATMOS. 77, 77.

Frances R. Havergal, 1836-1879   William H. Havergal, 1793-1870

In moderate time

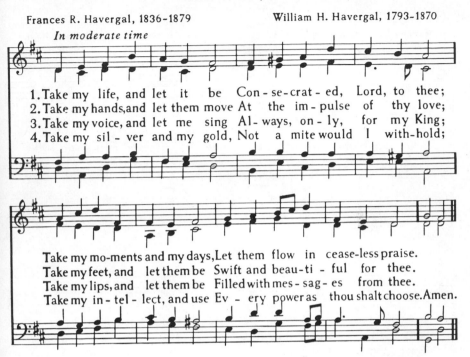

1. Take my life, and let it be Con - se - crat - ed, Lord, to thee;
2. Take my hands, and let them move At the im - pulse of thy love;
3. Take my voice, and let me sing Al - ways, on - ly, for my King;
4. Take my sil - ver and my gold, Not a mite would I with-hold;

Take my mo-ments and my days, Let them flow in cease-less praise.
Take my feet, and let them be Swift and beau-ti - ful for thee.
Take my lips, and let them be Filled with mes - sag - es from thee.
Take my in - tel - lect, and use Ev - ery power as thou shalt choose. Amen.

5. Take my will and make it thine,
   It shall be no longer mine;
   Take my heart, it is thine own,
   It shall be thy royal throne.

6. Take my love; my Lord, I pour
   At thy feet its treasure-store;
   Take myself, and I will be
   Ever, only, all for thee.

One of the great early churchmen, St. Hippolytus, once wrote, "The world is a sea, in which the church, like a ship, is beaten by the waves, but not submerged." First of all, the church is *people*, and not just the building we refer to when we say we are "going to church." But the idea of the ship appears in our church buildings as well. The part of the building where the pews are located is called the "nave," a word derived from the Latin word for "ship."

SERVICE

Lord, Speak to Me

CANONBURY. L. M.

Frances R. Havergal, 1836-1879

Robert Schumann, 1810-1856

In moderate time

1. Lord, speak to me, that I may speak In liv - ing ech - oes of thy tone; As thou hast sought, so let me seek Thy err - ing chil - dren lost and lone.

2. O lead me, Lord, that I may lead The wan-dering and the wa - vering feet; O feed me, Lord, that I may feed Thy hun-gering ones with man-na sweet.

3. O strength-en me, that while I stand Firm on the Rock, and strong in thee, I may stretch out a lov - ing hand To wres-tlers with the trou-bled sea.

4. O teach me, Lord, that I may teach The pre - cious things thou dost im - part; And wing my words, that they may reach The hid - den depths of many a heart.

5. O fill me with thy full - ness, Lord, Un - til my ver - y heart o'er - flow In kin - dling thought and glow-ing word Thy love to tell, thy praise to show. A - men.

The World One Neighborhood

176

ELLACOMBE. C. M. D.

Jeanette E. Perkins, 1887–1960

Württemberg *Gesangbuch,* 1784

Brightly

1. We thank thee, Lord, for eyes to see The beau-ty of the earth;
2. Help us re-mem-ber that to some The eye and ear and mind
3. O may our eyes be o-pen, Lord, To see our neigh-bors' need;

For ears to hear the words of love And hap-py sounds of mirth;
Bring sights and sounds of ug-li-ness And on-ly sad-ness find;
And may our ears be kept a-lert Their cries for help to heed;

For minds that find new thoughts to think, New won-ders to ex-plore;
Help us re-mem-ber that to them The world has seemed un-fair;
Make keen our minds to plan the best For one an-oth-er's good,

For health and free-dom to en-joy The good thou hast in store.
That we must strive to give to them The beau-ty all may share.
That all the world may be at last One friend-ly neigh-bor-hood.

177 O Master, Let Me Walk with Thee

MARYTON. L.M.

Washington Gladden, 1836-1918   Henry P. Smith, 1825-1898

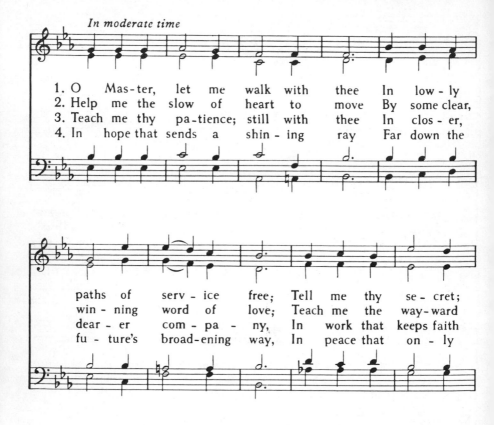

In moderate time

1. O Mas-ter, let me walk with thee In low-ly
2. Help me the slow of heart to move By some clear,
3. Teach me thy pa-tience; still with thee In clos-er,
4. In hope that sends a shin-ing ray Far down the

paths of serv-ice free; Tell me thy se-cret;
win-ning word of love; Teach me the way-ward
dear-er com-pa-ny, In work that keeps faith
fu-ture's broad-ening way, In peace that on-ly

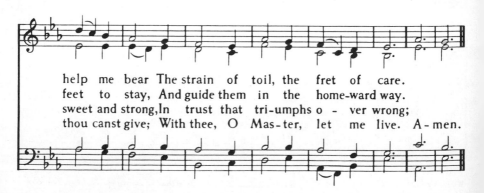

help me bear The strain of toil, the fret of care.
feet to stay, And guide them in the home-ward way.
sweet and strong, In trust that tri-umphs o-ver wrong;
thou canst give; With thee, O Mas-ter, let me live. A-men.

Blest Be the Tie That Binds

DENNIS. S. M.

John Fawcett, 1740-1817

Hans G. Naegeli, 1773-1836
Adapt. Lowell Mason, 1792-1872

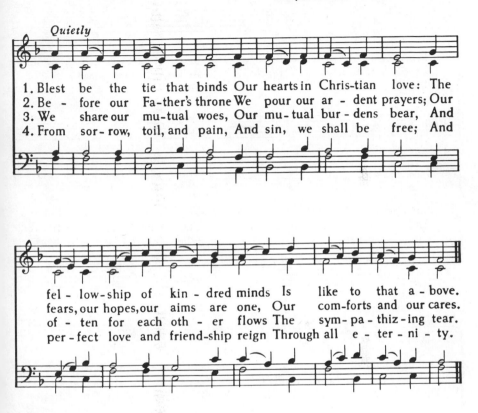

Quietly

1. Blest be the tie that binds Our hearts in Chris-tian love: The
2. Be - fore our Fa-ther's throne We pour our ar - dent prayers; Our
3. We share our mu-tual woes, Our mu-tual bur - dens bear, And
4. From sor-row, toil, and pain, And sin, we shall be free; And

fel - low-ship of kin - dred minds Is like to that a - bove.
fears, our hopes, our aims are one, Our com-forts and our cares.
of - ten for each oth - er flows The sym - pa - thiz - ing tear.
per - fect love and friend-ship reign Through all e - ter - ni - ty.

And Jesus said,
"Whoever would be great among you must be your servant, and whoever would be first among you must be slave of all. For the Son of Man also came not to be served but to serve, and to give his life as a ransom for many" (Mark 10:43-45).

Lead On, O King Eternal

179

LANCASHIRE. 76, 76. D.

Ernest W. Shurtleff, 1862-1917

Henry Smart, 1813-1879

In moderate time

1. Lead on, O King e - ter - nal, The day of march has come;
2. Lead on, O King e - ter - nal, Till sin's fierce war shall cease,
3. Lead on, O King e - ter - nal: We fol - low, not with fears,

Hence-forth in fields of con-quest Thy tents shall be our home:
And ho - li - ness shall whis- per The sweet A-men of peace;
For glad-ness breaks like morn-ing Wher-e'er thy face ap - pears:

Through days of prep - a - ra - tion Thy grace has made us strong,
For not with swords' loud clash- ing, Nor roll of stir-ring drums,
Thy Cross is lift - ed o'er us; We jour-ney in its light;

And now, O King e - ter - nal, We lift our bat -tle - song.
But deeds of love and mer - cy, The heaven-ly king-dom comes.
The crown a-waits the con-quest; Lead on, O God of might. A-men.

Stand Up, Stand Up for Jesus

180

WEBB. 76, 76. D.

George Duffield, 1818-1888   George J. Webb, 1803-1887

Broadly, with movement

1. Stand up, stand up for Je - sus, Ye sol-diers of the Cross;
2. Stand up, stand up for Je - sus, The trum-pet call o - bey;
3. Stand up, stand up for Je - sus, Stand in his strength a - lone;
4. Stand up, stand up for Je - sus, The strife will not be long;

Lift high his roy - al ban-ner, It must not suf-fer loss:
Forth to the might-y con-flict In this his glo-rious day:
The arm of flesh will fail you, Ye dare not trust your own:
This day the noise of bat - tle, The next the vic - tor's song:

From vic-tory un - to vic-tory His ar - my he shall lead,
Ye that are men, now serve him A - gainst un-num-bered foes;
Put on the gos - pel ar - mor, Each piece put on with prayer;
To him that o - ver - com-eth A crown of life shall be;

Till ev-ery foe is van-quished, And Christ is Lord in - deed.
Let cour-age rise with dan - ger, And strength to strength op - pose.
Where du - ty calls or dan - ger, Be nev - er want - ing there.
He with the King of Glo - ry Shall reign e - ter - nal - ly.

181 **Onward, Christian Soldiers**

ST. GERTRUDE. 65, 65. D. With Refrain.

Sabine Baring-Gould, 1834-1924   Arthur S. Sullivan, 1842-1900

Broadly

1. On - ward, Chris - tian sol - diers, March-ing as to war,
2. At the sign of tri - umph Sa - tan's le - gions flee;
3. Like a might - y ar - my Moves the church of God;
4. Crowns and thrones may per - ish, King-doms rise and wane,
5. On - ward, then, ye faith - ful, Join our hap - py throng;

With the Cross of Je - sus Go - ing on be - fore.
On then, Chris-tian sol - diers, On to vic - to - ry!
Broth-ers, we are tread - ing Where the saints have trod.
But the church of Je - sus Con - stant will re - main;
Blend with ours your voic - es, In the tri - umph - song;

Christ the roy - al Mas - ter Leads a - gainst the foe;
Hell's foun - da-tions quiv - er At the shout of praise;
We are not di - vid - ed, All one bod - y we,
Gates of hell can nev - er 'Gainst that church pre - vail;
Glo - ry, laud, and hon - or, Un - to Christ the King;

For - ward in - to bat - tle, See, his ban-ners go!
Broth-ers, lift your voic - es, Loud your an-thems raise.
One in hope and doc - trine, One in char - i - ty.
We have Christ's own prom-ise, And that can - not fail.
This through count-less a - ges Men and an - gels sing.

Music by permission of J. Curwen and Sons, Ltd., London.

Refrain

On-ward, Chris-tian sol - diers, March-ing as to war,

With the Cross of Je - sus Go - ing on be - fore.

Am I a Soldier of the Cross　182
ARLINGTON. C. M.

Isaac Watts, 1674-1748, *alt.*　　　　　　　Thomas A. Arne, 1710-1778

With vigor

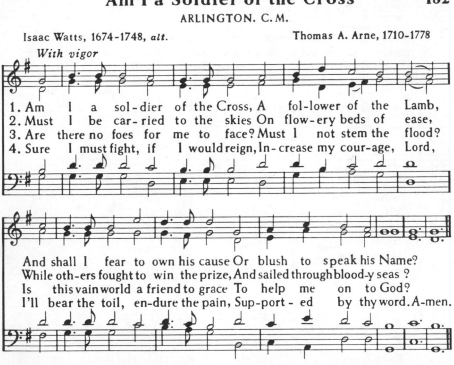

1. Am　I　a　sol-dier of the Cross, A　fol-lower of the　Lamb,
2. Must　I　be　car-ried　to the　skies On　flow-ery beds of　ease,
3. Are　there no foes for　me to　face? Must I　not stem the　flood?
4. Sure　I must fight, if　I would reign, In-crease my cour-age, Lord,

And shall I　fear to own his cause Or blush　to　speak his Name?
While oth-ers fought to　win the prize, And sailed through blood-y seas ?
Is　this vain world a friend to grace To　help　me　on　to God?
I'll　bear the toil, en-dure the pain, Sup-port - ed　by thy word. A-men.

5. Thy saints, in all this glorious war,
　Shall conquer, though they die;
　They see the triumph from afar,
　By faith they bring it nigh.

6. When that illustrious day shall rise,
　And all thy armies shine
　In robes of victory through the skies,
　The glory shall be thine.

This hymn may also be sung to WINCHESTER *(No. 45).*

183 **Rejoice, Ye Pure in Heart**

MARION. S. M. With Refrain.

Edward H. Plumptre, 1821-1891   Arthur H. Messiter, 1834-1916

With spirit

1. Re - joice, ye pure in heart, Re - joice, give thanks, and sing; Your fes - tal ban - ner wave on high, The Cross of Christ your King.
2. Bright youth and snow-crowned age, Strong men and maid - ens meek, Raise high your free ex - ult - ing song; God's won-drous prais - es speak.
3. With voice as full and strong As o - cean's surg - ing praise, Send forth the hymns our fa - thers loved. The psalms of an - cient days.
4. Still lift your stand - ard high, Still march in firm ar - ray, As war - riors through the dark - ness toil Till dawns the gold - en day.

Refrain

Re - joice, re - joice! Re - joice, give thanks, and sing!

Re - joice, re - joice!

How Firm a Foundation

184

ADESTE FIDELES. Irregular.

K in Rippon's *Selection*, 1787, alt.　　　　Wade's *Cantus diversi*, 1751

In moderate time

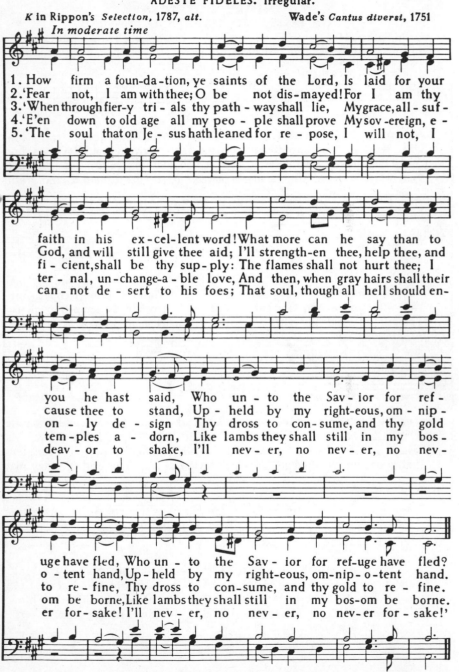

1. How firm a foun-da-tion, ye saints of the Lord, Is laid for your
2. 'Fear not, I am with thee; O be not dis-mayed! For I am thy
3. 'When through fier-y tri-als thy path-way shall lie, My grace, all-suf-
4. 'E'en down to old age all my peo-ple shall prove My sov-ereign, e-
5. 'The soul that on Je-sus hath leaned for re-pose, I will not, I

faith in his ex-cel-lent word! What more can he say than to
God, and will still give thee aid; I'll strength-en thee, help thee, and
fi-cient, shall be thy sup-ply: The flames shall not hurt thee; I
ter-nal, un-change-a-ble love, And then, when gray hairs shall their
can-not de-sert to his foes; That soul, though all hell should en-

you he hast said, Who un-to the Sav-ior for ref-
cause thee to stand, Up-held by my right-eous, om-nip-
on-ly de-sign Thy dross to con-sume, and thy gold
tem-ples a-dorn, Like lambs they shall still in my bos-
deav-or to shake, I'll nev-er, no nev-er, no nev-

uge have fled, Who un-to the Sav-ior for ref-uge have fled?
o-tent hand, Up-held by my right-eous, om-nip-o-tent hand.
to re-fine, Thy dross to con-sume, and thy gold to re-fine.
om be borne, Like lambs they shall still in my bos-om be borne.
er for-sake! I'll nev-er, no nev-er, no nev-er for-sake!'

Festivals
REFORMATION
A Mighty Fortress

185

EIN' FESTE BURG. 87, 87, 66, 66, 7.

Martin Luther, 1483-1546
Tr. Frederick H. Hedge, 1805-1890
Based on Psalm 46

Martin Luther, 1483-1546

Broadly, with vigor

1. A might-y for-tress is our God, A bul-wark nev-er fail - ing;
2. Did we in our own strength con-fide Our striv-ing would be los - ing;
3. And though this world, with dev - ils filled, Should threat-en to un-do us;
4. That word a-bove all earth - ly powers, No thanks to them, a - bid - eth;

Our help-er he a - mid the flood Of mor-tal ills pre-vail - ing:
Were not the right Man on our side, The Man of God's own choos - ing.
We will not fear, for God hath willed His truth to tri-umph through us:
The Spir-it and the gifts are ours Through him who with us sid - eth:

For still our an-cient foe Doth seek to work us woe; His craft and power are
Dost ask who that may be? Christ Je-sus, it is he; Lord Sab-a - oth his
The prince of dark-ness grim, We trem-ble not for him; His rage we can en-
Let goods and kin-dred go, This mor-tal life al-so; The bod-y they may

great, And, armed with cru-el hate, On earth is not his e - qual.
Name, From age to age the same, And he must win the bat - tle.
dure, For lo, his doom is sure! One lit - tle word shall fell him.
kill: God's truth a - bid-eth still, His king-dom is for ev - er.

Built on a Rock

KIRKEN. 88, 88, 88, 8.

Nikolai F. S. Grundtvig, 1783-1872
Tr. Carl Doving, 1867-1937
Revised, Fred C. M. Hansen, 1888-

Ludvig M. Lindeman, 1812-1887

With vigor

1. Built on a rock the church doth stand, E- ven when stee - ples are
2. Not in our tem-ples made with hands God the Al - might - y, is
3. We are God's house of liv - ing stones, Built for his own hab-i-
4. Yet in this house, an earth-ly frame, Je - sus the chil - dren is
5. Thro' all the pass-ing years, O Lord, Grant that when church bells are

fall - ing; Crum-bled have spires in ev - ery land, Bells still are
dwell - ing; High in the heavens his tem-ple stands, All earth-ly
ta - tion; He fills our hearts, his hum-ble thrones, Grant-ing us
bless - ing; Hith - er we come to praise his Name, Faith in our
ring - ing, Man - y may come to hear God's Word Where he this

chim-ing and call - ing; Call-ing the young and old to rest,
tem-ples ex - cel - ling; Yet he who dwells in heaven a - bove
life and sal - va - tion; Were two or three to seek his face,
Sav-ior con - fess - ing; Je - sus to us his Spir-it sent,
prom-ise is bring - ing: 'I know mine own, mine own know me,

Call - ing the souls of men dis-tressed, Long-ing for life ev - er - last - ing.
Deigns to a - bide with us in love, Mak-ing our bod-ies his tem - ple.
He in their midst would show his grace, Bless-ings up-on them be - stow - ing.
Mak - ing with us his cov - e - nant, Grant-ing his chil-dren the king - dom.
Ye, not the world, my face shall see; My peace I leave with you.' A - men.

HARVEST

187 **Come, Ye Thankful People, Come**

ST. GEORGE'S, WINDSOR. 77, 77. D.

Henry Alford, 1810-1871 George J. Elvey, 1816-1893

With spirit

1. Come, ye thank-ful peo-ple, come, Raise the song of har-vest-home;
2. All the world is God's own field, Fruit un-to his praise to yield;
3. For the Lord our God shall come, And shall take his har-vest home;
4. E-ven so, Lord, quick-ly come To thy fi-nal har-vest-home;

All is safe-ly gath-ered in Ere the win-ter storms be-gin;
Wheat and tares to-geth-er sown, Un-to joy or sor-row grown;
From his field shall in that day All of-fenc-es purge a-way;
Gath-er thou thy peo-ple in, Free from sor-row, free from sin,

God our Mak-er doth pro-vide For our wants to be sup-plied:
First the blade and then the ear, Then the full corn shall ap-pear:
Give his an-gels charge at last In the fire the tares to cast;
There for ev-er pu-ri-fied, In thy pres-ence to a-bide:

Come, to God's own tem-ple come, Raise the song of har-vest-home.
Lord of har-vest, grant that we Whole-some grain and pure may be.
But the fruit-ful ears to store In his gar-ner ev-er-more.
Come, with all thine an-gels, come, Raise the glo-rious har-vest-home. A-men.

Sing to the Lord of Harvest

WIE LIEBLICH IST DER MAIEN. 76, 76. D.

J. S. B. Monsell, 1811-1875   *Himmlische Harpffe Davids,* Nürnberg, 1581

In moderate time

1. Sing   to the Lord of   har-vest, Sing songs of love and praise;
2. By   him the clouds drop fat-ness, The   des-erts bloom and spring,
3. Heap   on   his sa - cred   al - tar The gifts his good-ness gave,

With joy - ful hearts and   voi-ces Your al - le - lu - ias raise!
The   hills leap up   in   glad-ness, The val - leys laugh and sing.
The   gold - en sheaves of   har-vest, The souls he died to   save.

By   him the roll - ing   sea-sons In fruit-ful or - der move;
He   fill - eth with his   full-ness All things with large in - crease;
Your hearts lay down be - fore him When at his feet ye   fall,

Sing   to the Lord of   har-vest A song of hap-py love.
He crowns the year with   good-ness, With plen - ty, and with peace.
And with your lives a - dore him Who gave his life for   all.

189 God Hath Given Us Harvest

ST. LUCIAN. 65, 65.

J. A. Davies   Johann C. H. Rinck, 1770-1846

In moderate time

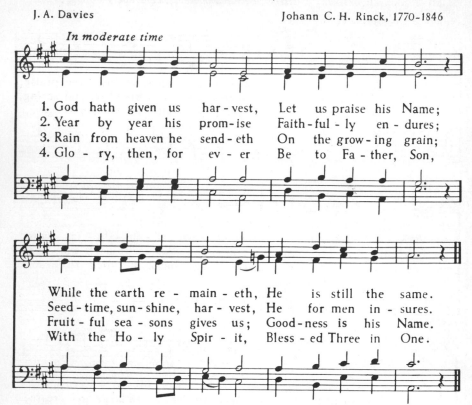

1. God hath given us har-vest, Let us praise his Name;
2. Year by year his prom-ise Faith-ful-ly en - dures;
3. Rain from heaven he send-eth On the grow-ing grain;
4. Glo - ry, then, for ev - er Be to Fa - ther, Son,

While the earth re - main-eth, He is still the same.
Seed-time, sun-shine, har - vest, He for men in - sures.
Fruit-ful sea - sons gives us; Good-ness is his Name.
With the Ho - ly Spir - it, Bless - ed Three in One.

Harmonization used by permission of Concordia Publishing House.

A sheaf of wheat represents the harvest when God opens his hand and gives us an abundance of good things to nourish our bodies. Wheat is also used to suggest the Bread of Life. "Jesus said to them, 'I am the bread of life; he who comes to me shall not hunger, and he who believes in me shall never thirst'" (John 6:35). Wheat and grapes used together symbolize bread and wine—the Body and Blood of Christ.

THANKSGIVING
Now Thank We All Our God

190

NUN DANKET ALLE GOTT. 67, 67, 66, 66.

Martin Rinkart, 1586-1649

Tr. Catherine Winkworth, 1829-1878

Johann Crüger, 1598-1662

Majestically

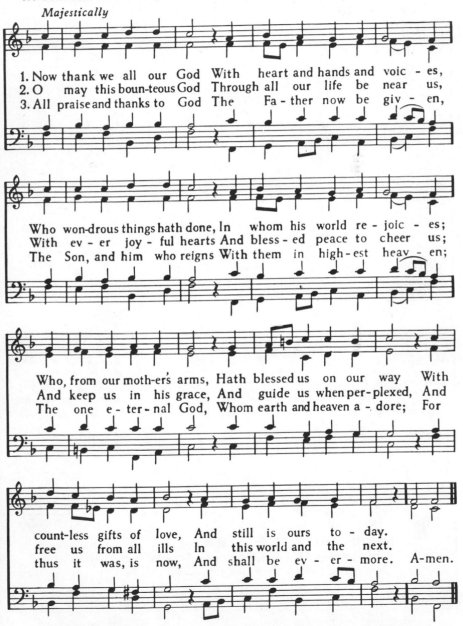

1. Now thank we all our God With heart and hands and voic - es,
2. O may this boun-teous God Through all our life be near us,
3. All praise and thanks to God The Fa - ther now be giv - en,

Who won-drous things hath done, In whom his world re - joic - es;
With ev - er joy - ful hearts And bless - ed peace to cheer us;
The Son, and him who reigns With them in high - est heav - en;

Who, from our moth-er's arms, Hath blessed us on our way With
And keep us in his grace, And guide us when per-plexed, And
The one e - ter - nal God, Whom earth and heaven a - dore; For

count-less gifts of love, And still is ours to - day.
free us from all ills In this world and the next.
thus it was, is now, And shall be ev - er - more. A-men.

191 ## We Praise Thee, O God

KREMSER. 12 11, 12 11.

Author unknown, 1626
Tr. Julia Cory, 1882~

Netherland Folk Song, XVII *cent*
Arr. Edward Kremser, 1838-1914

With breadth

1. We praise thee, O God our Re - deem - er, Cre - a - tor,
2. We wor - ship thee, God of our fa - thers, we bless thee;
3. With voic - es u - nit - ed our prais - es we of - fer,

In grate - ful de - vo - tion our trib - ute we bring.
Through trou - ble and tem - pest our guide thou hast been;
To thee, great Je - ho - vah, glad an - thems we raise;

We lay it be - fore thee, we kneel and a - dore thee,
When per - ils o'er - take us, es - cape thou wilt make us,
Thy strong arm will guide us, our God is be - side us;

We bless thy ho - ly Name, glad prais - es we bring.
And with thy help, O Lord, our bat - tles we win.
To thee, our great Re - deem - er, for ev - er be praise. A - men.

For the Beauty of the Earth

DIX (TREUER HEILAND). 77, 77, 77.

Folliott S. Pierpoint, 1835-1917   Conrad Kocher, 1786-1872

In moderate time

1. For the beau-ty of the earth, For the beau-ty of the skies,
2. For the beau-ty of each hour Of the day and of the night,
3. For the joy of ear and eye, For the heart and mind's de - light,
4. For the joy of hu-man love, Broth-er, sis - ter, par - ent, child,
5. For thy - self, best gift di - vine, To our race so free - ly given,

For   the love which from our birth O - ver and a-round us lies,
Hill   and vale, and tree and flower, Sun and moon and stars of light,
For   the mys - tic har - mo - ny Link-ing sense to sound and sight,
Friends on earth and friends a - bove, For all gen-tle thoughts and mild,
For   that great, great love of thine, Peace on earth and joy in heaven,

Christ, our God, to thee we raise This our sac - ri - fice of praise.
Christ, our God, to thee we raise This our sac - ri - fice of praise.
Christ, our God, to thee we raise This our sac - ri - fice of praise.
Christ, our God, to thee we raise This our sac - ri - fice of praise.
Christ, our God, to thee we raise This our sac - ri - fice of praise. A-men.

Words from SONGS OF PRAISE, ENLARGED EDITION *by permission of the Estate of the late F. S. Pierpoint and Oxford University Press.*
This hymn may also be sung to EASTER GLORY *(No. 63).*

193 ## O God, Our Help in Ages Past

ST. ANNE. C. M.

Isaac Watts, 1674-1748
Based on Psalm 90

William Croft, 1678-1727

With dignity

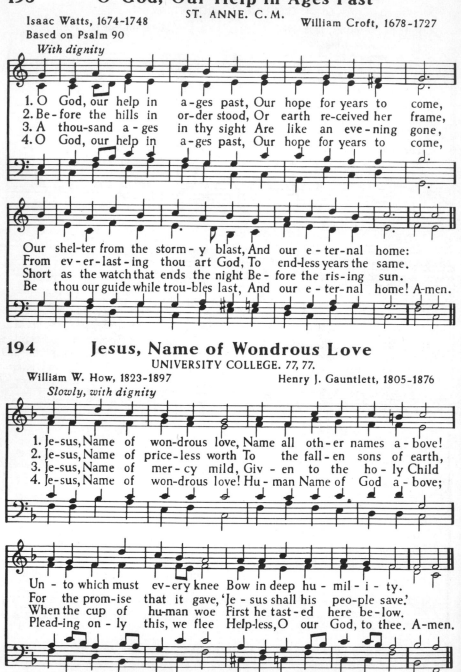

1. O God, our help in a-ges past, Our hope for years to come,
2. Be-fore the hills in or-der stood, Or earth re-ceived her frame,
3. A thou-sand a - ges in thy sight Are like an eve-ning gone,
4. O God, our help in a-ges past, Our hope for years to come,

Our shel-ter from the storm - y blast, And our e - ter-nal home:
From ev - er - last - ing thou art God, To end-less years the same.
Short as the watch that ends the night Be - fore the ris-ing sun.
Be thou our guide while trou-bles last, And our e - ter-nal home! A-men.

194 ## Jesus, Name of Wondrous Love

UNIVERSITY COLLEGE. 77, 77.

William W. How, 1823-1897

Henry J. Gauntlett, 1805-1876

Slowly, with dignity

1. Je-sus, Name of won-drous love, Name all oth-er names a-bove!
2. Je-sus, Name of price-less worth To the fall-en sons of earth,
3. Je-sus, Name of mer - cy mild, Giv - en to the ho - ly Child
4. Je-sus, Name of won-drous love! Hu - man Name of God a-bove;

Un - to which must ev-ery knee Bow in deep hu - mil - i - ty.
For the prom-ise that it gave, 'Je - sus shall his peo-ple save.'
When the cup of hu-man woe First he tast-ed here be-low.
Plead-ing on - ly this, we flee Help-less, O our God, to thee. A-men.

OUR COUNTRY
God of Our Fathers

NATIONAL HYMN. 10 10, 10 10.

Daniel C. Roberts, 1841-1907   George W. Warren, 1828-1902

With dignity

1. God of our fa - thers, whose al - might - y hand
2. Thy love di - vine hath led us in the past,
3. From war's a - larms, from dead - ly pes - ti - lence,
4. Re - fresh thy peo - ple on their toil - some way,

Leads forth in beau - ty all the star - ry band
In this free land by thee our lot is cast;
Be thy strong arm our ev - er sure de - fence;
Lead us from night to nev - er - end - ing day;

Of shin - ing worlds in splen - dor through the skies,
Be thou our rul - er, guard - ian, guide, and stay;
Thy true re - li - gion in our hearts in - crease,
Fill all our lives with love and grace di - vine,

Our grate - ful songs be - fore thy throne a - rise.
Thy word our law, thy paths our cho - sen way.
Thy boun - teous good - ness nour - ish us in peace.
And glo - ry, laud, and praise be ev - er thine. A - men.

196 Battle Hymn of the Republic

BATTLE HYMN. 15 15 15, 6. With Refrain.

Julia Ward Howe, 1819-1910

William Steffe, 1852

With strength

1. Mine eyes have seen the glo-ry of the com-ing of the Lord; He is tramp-ling out the vin-tage where the grapes of wrath are stored; He hath loosed the fate-ful light-ning of his ter-ri-ble swift sword: His truth is march-ing on.

2. He has sound-ed forth the trum-pet that shall nev-er call re-treat; He is sift-ing out the hearts of men be-fore his judg-ment-seat; O be swift, my soul, to an-swer him; be ju-bi-lant my feet! Our God is march-ing on.

3. In the beau-ty of the lil-ies Christ was born a-cross the sea, With a glo-ry in his bos-om that trans-fig-ures you and me: As he died to make men ho-ly, let us die to make men free, While God is march-ing on.

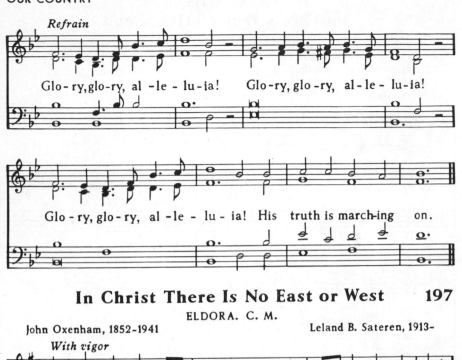

Refrain

Glo - ry, glo - ry, al - le - lu - ia! Glo - ry, glo - ry, al - le - lu - ia!

Glo - ry, glo - ry, al - le - lu - ia! His truth is march-ing on.

In Christ There Is No East or West 197

ELDORA. C. M.

John Oxenham, 1852-1941   Leland B. Sateren, 1913-

With vigor

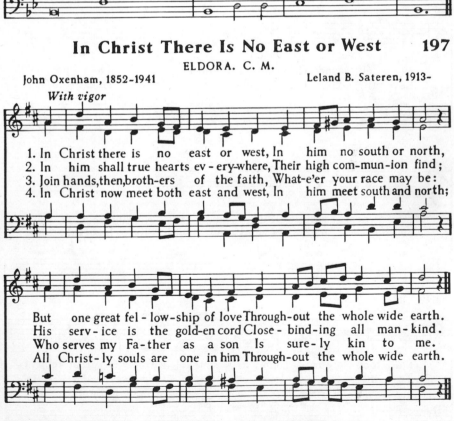

1. In Christ there is no east or west, In him no south or north,
2. In him shall true hearts ev - ery-where, Their high com-mun-ion find;
3. Join hands, then, broth-ers of the faith, What-e'er your race may be:
4. In Christ now meet both east and west, In him meet south and north;

But one great fel - low-ship of love Through-out the whole wide earth.
His serv - ice is the gold-en cord Close - bind-ing all man - kind.
Who serves my Fa - ther as a son Is sure - ly kin to me.
All Christ-ly souls are one in him Through-out the whole wide earth.

NATIONAL

198 ## God Bless Our Native Land

NATIONAL ANTHEM. 664, 6664.

Based on a German Hymn
by Siegfried A. Mahlmann, 1771 - 1826
Charles T. Brooks, 1813 - 1883
John S. Dwight, 1813 - 1893

Thesaurus Musicus, 1744

Slowly, with dignity

1. God bless our na - tive land; Firm may she
2. For her our prayers shall rise To God a -

ev - er stand Through storm and night: When the wild
bove the skies; On him we wait. Thou who art

tem - pests rave, Rul - er of wind and wave,
ev - er nigh, Guard - ing with watch - ful eye,

Do thou our coun - try save By thy great might.
To thee a - loud we cry, God save the state!

America 199
Tune: NATIONAL ANTHEM (No. 198).

1. My country, 'tis of thee,
   Sweet land of liberty,
   Of thee I sing:
   Land where my fathers died,
   Land of the pilgrims' pride,
   From every mountain side
   Let freedom ring.

2. My native country, thee,
   Land of the noble free,
   Thy name I love;
   I love thy rocks and rills,
   Thy woods and templed hills;
   My heart with rapture thrills
   Like that above.

3. Let music swell the breeze,
   And ring from all the trees
   Sweet freedom's song;
   Let mortal tongues awake;
   Let all that breathe partake;
   Let rocks their silence break,
   The sound prolong.

4. Our fathers' God, to thee,
   Author of liberty,
   To thee we sing:
   Long may our land be bright
   With freedom's holy light;
   Protect us by thy might,
   Great God, our King. Amen.

Samuel F. Smith, 1809-1895

God Save Our Gracious Queen 200
Tune: NATIONAL ANTHEM (No. 198).

1. God save our gracious Queen,
   Long live our noble Queen,
   God save the Queen:
   Send her victorious,
   Happy and glorious,
   Long to reign over us;
   God save the Queen.

2. Thy choicest gifts in store
   On her be pleased to pour;
   Long may she reign:
   May she defend our laws,
   And ever give us cause
   To sing with heart and voice,
   God save the Queen. Amen.

Author unknown, XVIII cent.

For the churches within the British Commonwealth.

America and *God Save Our Gracious Queen* are more than patriotic songs. In the best sense they are hymns of faith and prayer.

When we sing our national hymns we stand and confess that God is the Lord. We confess him not only as Lord of his kingdom and his believing people; here we publicly confess him as Lord of the nations, Lord of all men, Lord of his whole creation.

In the strength of this faith we pray for our rulers and governors, for ourselves and for all our fellow-citizens. With the singing of our national hymns we pray as we do in the Prayer of the Church:

"Preserve our Nation in righteousness and honor,
and continue thy blessings to us as a people,
that we may lead a quiet and peaceable life, in
all godliness and honesty."

Advent Tells Us Christ Is Near

NUN KOMM, DER HEIDEN HEILAND. 77, 77.

Katherine Hankey, 1834-1911

Geistliches Gesangbüchlein,
Wittenberg, 1524, *adapted*

Moderately

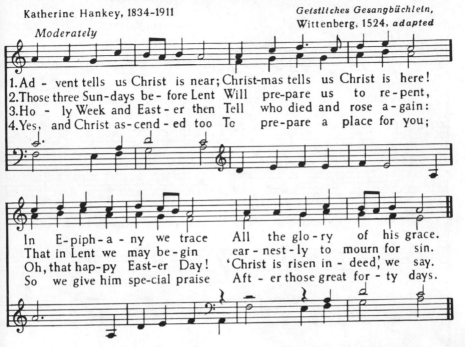

1. Ad - vent tells us Christ is near; Christ-mas tells us Christ is here!
2. Those three Sun-days be - fore Lent Will pre-pare us to re-pent,
3. Ho - ly Week and East - er then Tell who died and rose a - gain:
4. Yes, and Christ as-cend - ed too To pre-pare a place for you;

In E-piph-a-ny we trace All the glo-ry of his grace.
That in Lent we may be-gin ear-nest-ly to mourn for sin.
Oh, that hap-py East-er Day! 'Christ is risen in-deed,' we say.
So we give him spe-cial praise Aft-er those great for-ty days.

5. Then he sent the Holy Ghost
   On the day of Pentecost,
   With us ever to abide:
   Well may we keep Whitsuntide!

6. Last of all, we humbly sing
   Glory to our God and King,
   Glory to the One in Three
   On the Feast of Trinity.

Harmonization used by permission of Concordia Publishing House.
Small children may learn one verse during each appropriate season of the Church Year.

The Chi Rho (pronounced kī-rō) is one of several monograms which represent the name of our Savior. XP comes from the first two letters of ΧΡΙΣΤΟΣ, the Greek word for *Christ*.

202 All Things Bright and Beautiful

ROYAL OAK. 76, 76. D.

Cecil F. Alexander, 1818-1895

Old English Melody
Adapt. Martin Shaw, 1875-1958

Moderately

1. All things bright and beau-ti-ful, All crea-tures great and small,

All things wise and won-der-ful, The Lord God made them all.

2. Each lit-tle flower that o-pens, Each lit-tle bird that sings,
3. The pur-ple-head-ed moun-tain, The riv-er run-ning by,
4. The cold wind in the win-ter, The pleas-ant sum-mer sun,
5. He gave us eyes to see them, And lips that we might tell

He made their glow-ing col-ors, He made their ti-ny wings.
The sun-set, and the morn-ing That bright-ens up the sky,
The ripe fruits in the gar-den, He made them ev-ery one.
How great is God Al-might-y, Who has made all things well.

Go, Tell It on the Mountains

Negro Spiritual

Negro Spiritual
Harm. Comfort Hinderlie Dale

Joyously

1. When I was a learn-er, I sought both night and day,
2. He made me a watch-man Up-on the cit-y wall

I asked the Lord to aid me And he showed me the way.
An' if I am a Chris-tian, I am the least of all.

Go, tell it on the moun-tains, O-ver the hills an' ev-'ry-where,
Go, tell it on the moun-tains, O-ver the hills an' ev-'ry-where,

Go, tell it on the moun-tains That Je-sus Christ is born.
Go, tell it on the moun-tains That Je-sus Christ is born.

204 # I Was Made a Christian

HERMAS. 65, 65. D.

John S. Jones, *cir.* 1880

Frances R. Havergal, 1836–1879

Brightly

1. I was made a Chris-tian When my name was given,
2. I must, like a Chris-tian, Shun all e - vil ways,
3. All a Chris-tian's bless-ings I will claim for mine:

One of God's dear chil-dren And an heir of heaven.
Keep my faith in Je - sus, Serve him all my days.
Ho - ly work and wor-ship, Fel - low-ship di - vine.

In the name of Chris-tian I will glo - ry now,
Called to be a Chris-tian, I will praise the Lord,
Fa - ther, Son, and Spir - it, Give me grace that I

Ev - er-more re - mem - ber My bap-tis - mal vow.
Seek for his as - sist - ance So to keep my word.
Now may live a Chris - tian, And a Chris-tian die.

Once upon a Hillside

Calvin W. Laufer, *d.* 1938   Calvin W. Laufer, *d.* 1938

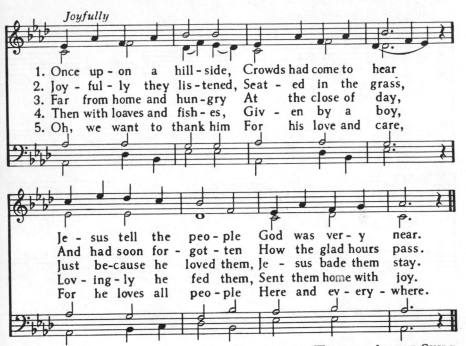

Joyfully

1. Once up-on a hill-side, Crowds had come to hear
2. Joy-ful-ly they lis-tened, Seat-ed in the grass,
3. Far from home and hun-gry At the close of day,
4. Then with loaves and fish-es, Giv-en by a boy,
5. Oh, we want to thank him For his love and care,

Je-sus tell the peo-ple God was ver-y near.
And had soon for-got-ten How the glad hours pass.
Just be-cause he loved them, Je-sus bade them stay.
Lov-ing-ly he fed them, Sent them home with joy.
For he loves all peo-ple Here and ev-ery-where.

Words and music copyright, 1935, by Calvin W. Laufer, from WHEN THE LITTLE CHILD
WANTS TO SING. *Used by permission.*

We Can Bring Gifts

Marie Pooler, 1928-   Marie Pooler, 1928-

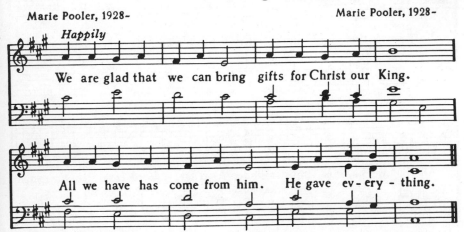

Happily

We are glad that we can bring gifts for Christ our King.

All we have has come from him. He gave ev-ery-thing.

From A CHILD SINGS, *copyright Augsburg Publishing House.*

OFFERTORY
We Give Thee But Thine Own

207

HEATH. S. M.

FIRST TUNE

William W. How, 1823-1897

Mason and Webb's *Cantica Laudis*, 1850

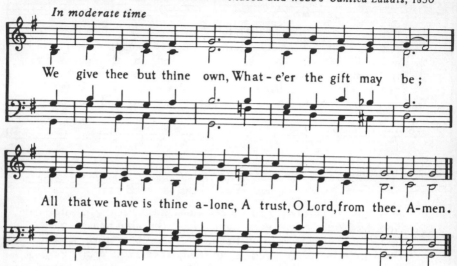

In moderate time

We give thee but thine own, What-e'er the gift may be;

All that we have is thine a-lone, A trust, O Lord, from thee. A-men.

207
We Give Thee But Thine Own

ST. GEORGE (ST. OLAVE). S. M.

SECOND TUNE

William W. How, 1823-1897

Henry J. Gauntlett, 1805-1876

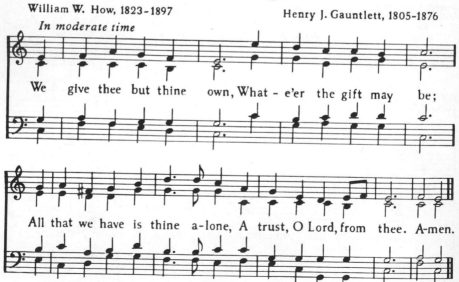

In moderate time

We give thee but thine own, What-e'er the gift may be;

All that we have is thine a-lone, A trust, O Lord, from thee. A-men.

God Is Great, God Is Good 208

The Hampton Grace, alt.   Marie Pooler

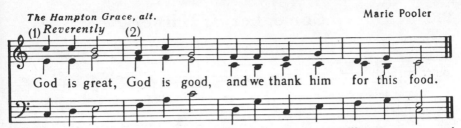

God is great, God is good, and we thank him for this food.

This may be sung as a two-part round using entrances indicated. When sung as a round, omit accompaniment.
Music copyright Augsburg Publishing House.

Be Present at Our Table, Lord 209
Tune: OLD HUNDREDTH (No. 226).

Be present at our table, Lord;
Be here and everywhere adored.
These mercies bless, and grant that we
May feast in paradise with thee.

Isaac Watts, 1674-1748

Be Present Here, Most Gracious God 210
Tune: DUNDEE (No. 98).

Be present here, most gracious God,
From whom all goodness springs.
Make clean our hearts, and feed our souls
On good and joyful things.

For Health and Strength, and Daily Food 211

Traditional

For health and strength, and dai-ly food, We praise thy Name, O Lord.

By permission of J. Curwen & Sons, Ltd., London.

O Give Thanks 212

Traditional

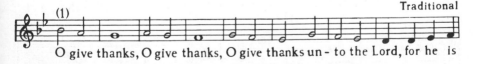

O give thanks, O give thanks, O give thanks un-to the Lord, for he is

gra-cious and his mer-cy en-dur-eth, en-dur-eth for ev-er.

ROUNDS

213   Come, Let Us Gather

Come, let us gath-er, now to sing Prais-es and thanks to
God our King. God's love sur-pass-es ev-ery-thing.

Traditional

214   Praise and Thanksgiving

Paraphrase of the German

Alsatian Round

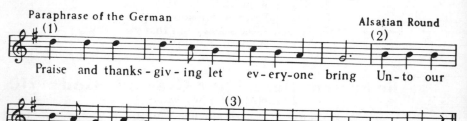

Praise and thanks-giv-ing let ev-ery-one bring Un-to our
Fa-ther for ev-ery good thing! All to-geth-er joy-ful-ly sing!

From THE WHOLE WORLD SINGING *by Edith Lovell Thomas, copyright Friendship Press. Used by permission.*

215   O Jesus, Sweet Jesus

Anna L. Marsh

From *The Diapason*, 1860
Ed., George F. Root, 1820-1895

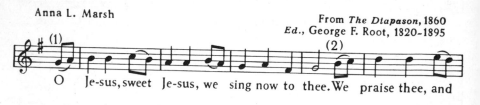

O Je-sus, sweet Je-sus, we sing now to thee. We praise thee, and
thank thee for all that we see. Je-sus makes us hap-py and free.

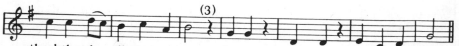

From THIRTY-FIVE SACRED ROUNDS AND CANONS, *by permission of Canyon Press.*

I Was Glad 216

Psalm 122:1

Olaf C. Christiansen

I was glad when they said un-to me: Let us go in-to the house of the
Lord. Our feet shall stand with-in thy gates, O Je-ru-sa-lem.

He That Dwelleth in the Secret Place 217

Psalm 91:1

Leland B. Sateren

He that dwell-eth in the se-cret place of the Most
High: shall a-bide un-der the shad-ow of the Al-might-y.

I Am the Light of the World 218

John 8:12

Marie Pooler

I am the light of the world. I am the light of the world.

Nos. 216 and 217: Melodies from INTROITS AND GRADUALS, *Series B, copyright Augsburg Publishing House.*

219 **To You Is Born This Day**

Luke 2:11

Marie Pooler

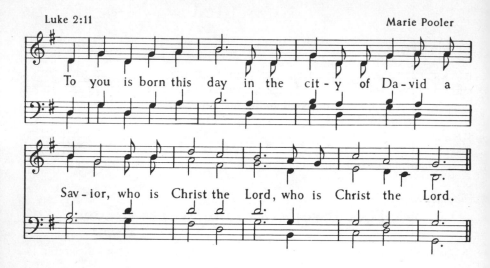

To you is born this day in the cit-y of Da-vid a
Sav-ior, who is Christ the Lord, who is Christ the Lord.

220 **For unto Us a Child Is Born**

Isaiah 9:6

Paul Christiansen

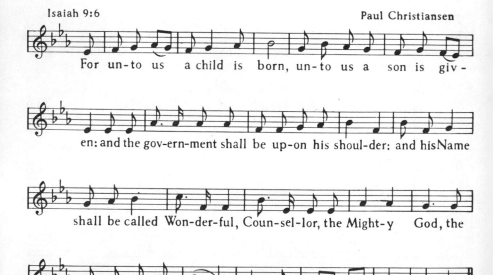

For un-to us a child is born, un-to us a son is giv-
en: and the gov-ern-ment shall be up-on his shoul-der: and his Name
shall be called Won-der-ful, Coun-sel-lor, the Might-y God, the
Ev-er-last-ing Fa - ther, the Prince of Peace.

Music on this page copyright Augsburg Publishing House.

He Shall Feed His Flock 221

Isaiah 40:11

From Handel's *Messiah*

He shall feed his flock like a shep - herd, and he shall gath - er the lambs with his arm.

If with All Your Hearts 222

Based on Jeremiah 29:13

From Mendelssohn's *Elijah*

If with all your hearts ye tru - ly seek me, ye shall ev - er sure - ly find me. Thus saith our God.

But the Lord Is Mindful of His Own 223

Based on Psalm 115:12

From Mendelssohn's *St. Paul*

But the Lord is mind - ful of his own, He re - mem-bers his chil - dren.

" 'I am the good shepherd. The good shepherd lays down his life for the sheep. He who is a hireling and not a shepherd . . . sees the wolf coming and leaves the sheep and flees; and the wolf snatches them and scatters them. . . . I am the good shepherd; I know my own and my own know me, as the Father knows me and I know the Father; and I lay down my life for the sheep' " (John 10: 11-15).

RESPONSE
Create in Me a Clean Heart

224

Psalm 51:10-12

Melody by J. A. Freylinghausen
Adapt. Harold W. Gilbert

Smoothly

Cre - ate in me a clean heart, O God: and re - new a right spir - it with - in me. Cast me not a - way from thy pres - ence: and take not thy Ho - ly Spir - it from me. Re - store un - to me the joy of thy sal - va - tion: and up - hold me with thy free Spir - it.

Gloria Patri

Henry Smart, 1813-1879

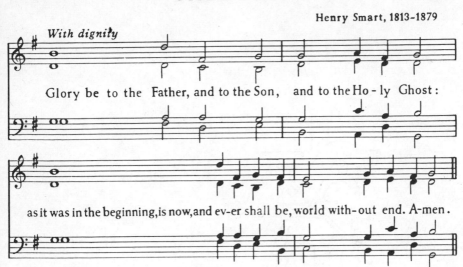

With dignity

Glory be to the Father, and to the Son, and to the Ho-ly Ghost: as it was in the beginning, is now, and ev-er shall be, world with-out end. A-men.

Doxology

OLD HUNDREDTH. L. M.

Thomas Ken, 1637-1711

Louis Bourgeois, *ctr.* 1510-1561
Genevan Psalter, 1551

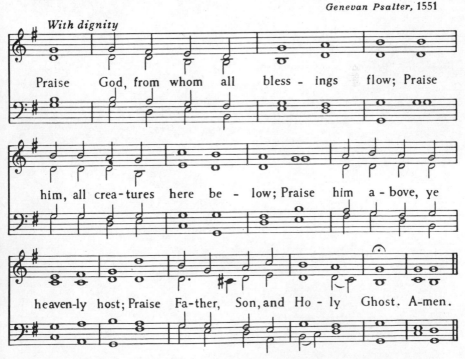

With dignity

Praise God, from whom all bless-ings flow; Praise him, all crea-tures here be-low; Praise him a-bove, ye heaven-ly host; Praise Fa-ther, Son, and Ho-ly Ghost. A-men.

FOR SMALL CHILDREN
God Who Made the Earth 227

Sarah B. Rhodes

Donald S. Barrows, *alt.*

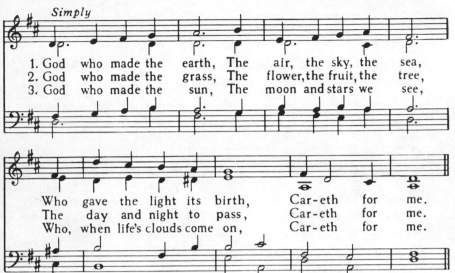

Simply

1. God who made the earth, The air, the sky, the sea,
2. God who made the grass, The flower, the fruit, the tree,
3. God who made the sun, The moon and stars we see,

Who gave the light its birth, Car-eth for me.
The day and night to pass, Car-eth for me.
Who, when life's clouds come on, Car-eth for me.

Music copyright 1942 by the Church Pension Fund.

Let Me Learn of Jesus 228

Fanny J. Crosby

J. F. Swift

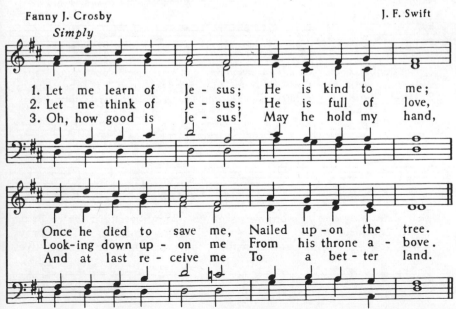

Simply

1. Let me learn of Je - sus; He is kind to me;
2. Let me think of Je - sus; He is full of love,
3. Oh, how good is Je - sus! May he hold my hand,

Once he died to save me, Nailed up - on the tree.
Look-ing down up - on me From his throne a - bove.
And at last re - ceive me To a bet - ter land.

O come, let us worship and bow down, let us kneel before the Lord, our Maker.
Psalm 95:6.

229   Father, We Thank Thee for the Night

Rebecca J. Weston

Daniel Batchellor

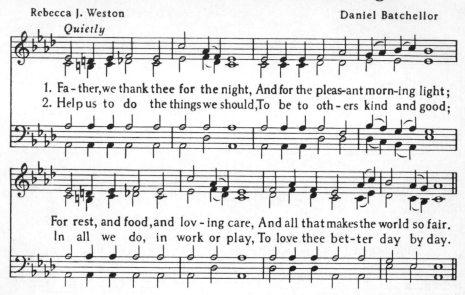

1. Fa-ther, we thank thee for the night, And for the pleas-ant morn-ing light;
2. Help us to do the things we should, To be to oth-ers kind and good;

For rest, and food, and lov-ing care, And all that makes the world so fair.
In all we do, in work or play, To love thee bet-ter day by day.

230   Father, Bless Our School Today

Anonymous

Freylinghausen's *Gesangbuch*, 1704

1. Fa-ther, bless our school to-day; Be in all we do and say;
2. Je-sus, well be-lov-ed Son, May thy will by us be done;
3. Ho-ly Spir-it, might-y Power, Con-se-crate this Lord's day hour;

Be in ev-ery song we sing, Ev-ery prayer to thee we bring.
Come and meet with us to-day; Teach us, Lord, thy-self, we pray.
Un-to us thine unc-tion give; Touch our souls that we may live.

This Is God's House 231

Louise M. Oglevee

W. G. Oglevee

Reverently

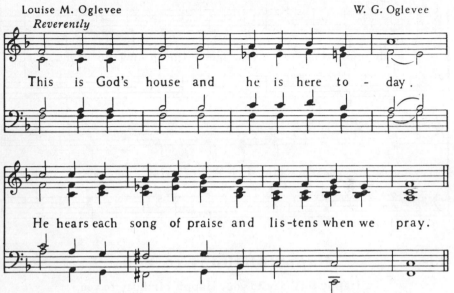

This is God's house and he is here to-day.

He hears each song of praise and lis-tens when we pray.

From SONGS FOR LITTLE PEOPLE by *Danielson and Conant. Copyright, The Pilgrim Press. Used by permission.*

Very Softly I Will Walk 232

Caroline Kellogg

Dorothy West

Quietly

Ver-y soft-ly I will walk, Ver-y gen-tly I will talk, When to church I go.

Though I can-not see him there, God is with me ev-ery-where; He is here, I know.

By permission of the American Baptist Publication Society.

I came that you may have life.   *John 10:10 b (paraphrase).*

233

Good Morning

Good morn-ing to you, Good morn-ing to you, Good

morn-ing, dear chil-dren, We're glad to see you.

234

Happy Birthday to You

Happy birthday to you, Happy birthday to you,
Happy birthday, dear_____, May Jesus bless you.

235   ## May Christ Be at Your Side Today

Clarence H. Koehler, *alt.*   *Genevan Psalter,* 1551

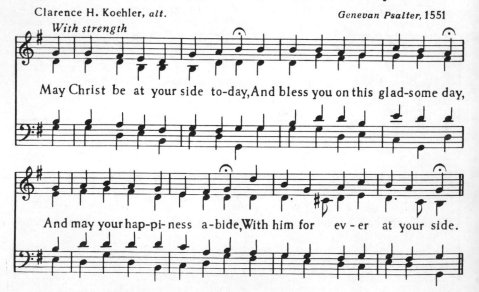

May Christ be at your side to-day, And bless you on this glad-some day,

And may your hap-pi-ness a-bide, With him for ev-er at your side.

Praise Him, Praise Him   236

Anonymous   Anonymous

Joyfully

1. Praise him, praise him, all ye lit-tle chil-dren; God is love, God is love;
2. Love him, love him, all ye lit-tle chil-dren; God is love, God is love;
3. Thank him, thank him, all ye lit-tle chil-dren; God is love, God is love;
4. Serve him, serve him, all ye lit-tle chil-dren; God is love, God is love;

Praise him, praise him, all ye lit-tle chil-dren; God is love, God is love.
Love him, love him, all ye lit-tle chil-dren; God is love, God is love.
Thank him, thank him, all ye lit-tle chil-dren; God is love, God is love.
Serve him, serve him, all ye lit-tle chil-dren; God is love, God is love.

Two Little Eyes   237

S. V. R. Ford

Anonymous

Simply

Two lit-tle eyes to look to God, Two lit-tle ears to hear his Word,
One lit-tle tongue to speak his truth, One lit-tle heart for him in youth;

Two lit-tle feet to walk his ways, Hands to serve him all my days.
Take them, O Je-sus, let them be Al-ways will-ing, true to thee.

238

Jesus Loves Me

Anna B. Warner

William B. Bradbury

1. Je-sus loves me! This I know For the Bi-ble tells me so;
2. Je-sus loves me! He who died, Heav-en's gates to o-pen wide;
3. Je-sus loves me! He will stay Close be-side me, all the way;

Lit-tle ones to him be-long, They are weak, but he is strong.
He will wash a-way my sin, Let his lit-tle child come in.
If I love him when I die, He will take me home on high.

Refrain

Yes, Je-sus loves me! Yes, Je-sus loves me!

Yes, Je-sus loves me! The Bi-ble tells me so.

The Father himself loves you. John 16:27a.

Lord, Teach a Little Child to Pray 239

Ascribed to Jane Taylor

F. Melius Christiansen

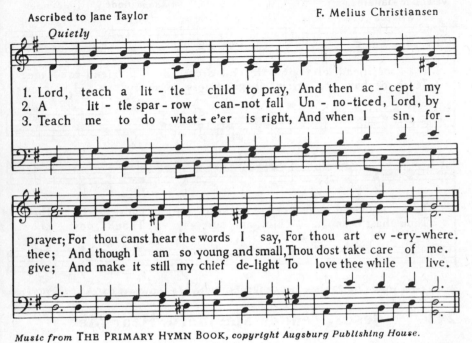

1. Lord, teach a lit-tle child to pray, And then ac-cept my
2. A lit-tle spar-row can-not fall Un-no-ticed, Lord, by
3. Teach me to do what-e'er is right, And when I sin, for-

prayer; For thou canst hear the words I say, For thou art ev-ery-where.
thee; And though I am so young and small, Thou dost take care of me.
give; And make it still my chief de-light To love thee while I live.

Music from THE PRIMARY HYMN BOOK, *copyright Augsburg Publishing House.*

Jesus Is My Shepherd 240

Minnie A. G. Edington

Johann C. H. Rinck

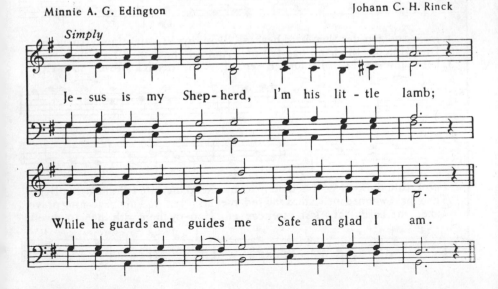

Je-sus is my Shep-herd, I'm his lit-tle lamb;

While he guards and guides me Safe and glad I am.

241   **Jesus, Friend of Little Children**

Walter J. Mathams   *Adapt. from* J. H. Maunder

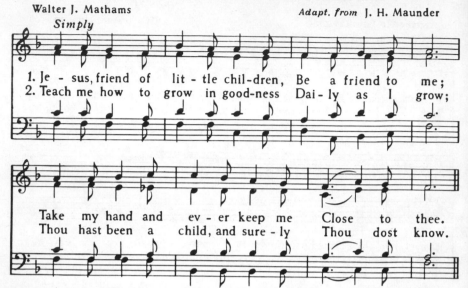

1. Je - sus, friend of lit - tle chil-dren, Be a friend to me;
2. Teach me how to grow in good-ness Dai - ly as I grow;

Take my hand and ev - er keep me Close to thee.
Thou hast been a child, and sure - ly Thou dost know.

Words from SONGS OF PRAISE, ENLARGED EDITION, *by permission of Oxford University Press.*

242   **Jesus, Tender Shepherd, Hear Me**

Mary L. Duncan   John Stainer

Quietly

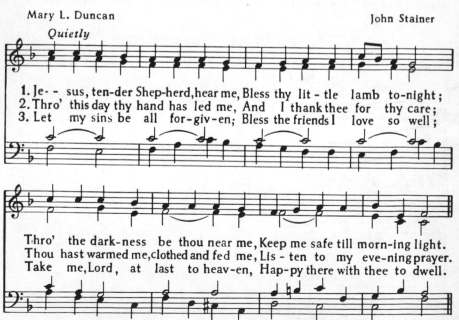

1. Je - - sus, ten-der Shep-herd, hear me, Bless thy lit - tle lamb to-night;
2. Thro' this day thy hand has led me, And I thank thee for thy care;
3. Let my sins be all for-giv-en; Bless the friends I love so well;

Thro' the dark-ness be thou near me, Keep me safe till morn-ing light.
Thou hast warmed me, clothed and fed me, Lis - ten to my eve-ning prayer.
Take me, Lord, at last to heav-en, Hap-py there with thee to dwell.

We love, because he first loved us. I John 4:19.

What Can I Give Him

243

Christina G. Rossetti

Danish Folk Song
Adapt. Grace W. Conant

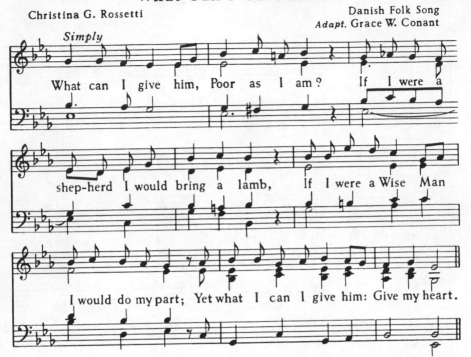

Simply

What can I give him, Poor as I am? If I were a

shep-herd I would bring a lamb, If I were a Wise Man

I would do my part; Yet what I can I give him: Give my heart.

Words from POETICAL WORKS *of Christina Rosetti.* Music from SONGS FOR LITTLE PEOPLE
by Danielson and Conant. Copyright The Pilgrim Press. Used by permission.

Jesus, Tender Savior

244

Melody No. 245
Jesus, tender Savior, Thou hast died for me;
Make me very thankful In my heart to thee.
The New Sunday School Hymnal, 1863

The fish is a kind of crossword puzzle. In Greek, the word for fish is ΙΧΘΥΣ (pronounced ikthus). The early Christians took each letter of this word and formed this acrostic:

$Ιησοῦς$ = Jesus

$Χριστός$ = Christ

$Θεοῦ$ = of God

$Υἱος$ = Son

$Σωτήρ$ = Savior

245

As Each Happy Christmas

Johann Wilhelm Hey
Tr. Harriet Spaeth

Johann C. H. Rinck

Joyfully

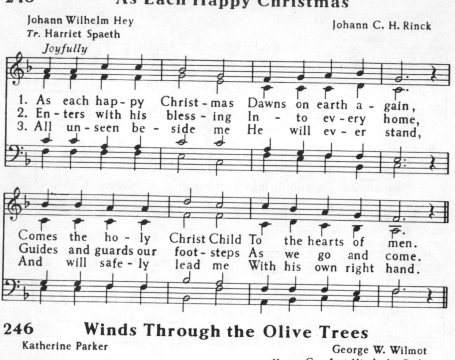

1. As each hap-py Christ-mas Dawns on earth a-gain,
2. En-ters with his bless-ing In-to ev-ery home,
3. All un-seen be-side me He will ev-er stand,

Comes the ho-ly Christ Child To the hearts of men.
Guides and guards our foot-steps As we go and come.
And will safe-ly lead me With his own right hand.

246   # Winds Through the Olive Trees

Katherine Parker

George W. Wilmot
Harm. Comfort Hinderlie Dale

Quietly

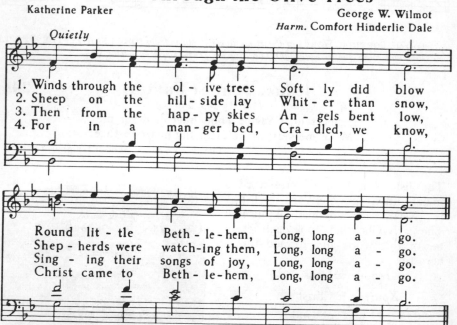

1. Winds through the ol-ive trees Soft-ly did blow
2. Sheep on the hill-side lay Whit-er than snow,
3. Then from the hap-py skies An-gels bent low,
4. For in a man-ger bed, Cra-dled, we know,

Round lit-tle Beth-le-hem, Long, long a-go.
Shep-herds were watch-ing them, Long, long a-go.
Sing-ing their songs of joy, Long, long a-go.
Christ came to Beth-le-hem, Long, long a-go.

Thou Who Once on Mother's Knee 247

F. T. Palgrave

Johann G. Ebeling
Harm. Robert Wetzler

Quietly

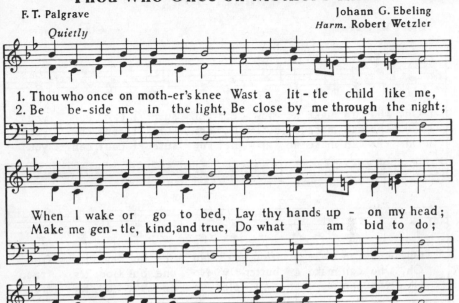

1. Thou who once on moth-er's knee Wast a lit-tle child like me,
2. Be be-side me in the light, Be close by me through the night;

When I wake or go to bed, Lay thy hands up - on my head;
Make me gen-tle, kind, and true, Do what I am bid to do;

Let me feel thee ver-y near, Je - sus Christ, my Sav-ior dear.
Help and cheer me when I fret, And for-give when I for-get.

Harmonization copyright Augsburg Publishing House.

He Prayeth Best 248

Samuel Coleridge

Marie Pooler

Simply

He pray-eth best who lov-eth best all things, both great and small.

For the dear Lord who lov-eth us, he made and lov-eth all.

Music copyright Augsburg Publishing House.

249   **Wonder Song**

Grace W. Owens   Clara L. Parker

Simply

1. Oh, who can make a flow-er? I'm sure I can't, can you?
2. Oh, who can make a butter-fly? I'm sure I can't, can you?
3. Oh, who can make an ap-ple? I'm sure I can't, can you?

Oh, who can make a flow-er? No one but God, 'tis true.
Oh, who can make a butter-fly? No one but God, 'tis true.
Oh, who can make an ap-ple? No one but God, 'tis true.

From SONGS FOR THE PRE-SCHOOL AGE, *by permission of Broadman Press.*

250   **The Easter King**

Marie Pooler   Marie Pooler

Joyfully

Let all lit-tle chil-dren sing glo-ry to the East-er King.

Je-sus lives! Je-sus lives! Je-sus is our East-er King!

From A CHILD SINGS, *copyright Augsburg Publishing House.*

He is not here; for he has risen, as he said. Matthew 28:6a.

We Welcome Glad Easter

Anonymous

Welsh Hymn Melody

Joyfully

1. We wel-come glad East - er when Je - sus a - rose
2. And tell how three Mar - ys came ear - ly that day
3. And sing of the an - gel who said: 'Do not fear!
4. So think of the prom-ise which Je - sus did give,

And won a great vic - to - ry o - ver his foes.
And there at the tomb found the stone rolled a - way.
Your Sav - ior is ris'n a - gain; He is not here?
That he who be - lieves in him al - so shall live.

Then raise your glad voi - ces, ye chil - dren, and sing,
Then raise your glad voi - ces, ye chil - dren, and sing,
Then raise your glad voi - ces, ye chil - dren, and sing,
Then raise your glad voi - ces, ye chil - dren, and sing,

Bring sweet East - er prais - es to Je - sus, our King.
Bring sweet East - er prais - es to Je - sus, our King.
Bring sweet East - er prais - es to Je - sus, our King.
Bring sweet East - er prais - es to Je - sus, our King.

252 God's Child

Marie Pooler

Marie Pooler

Gaily

1. I'm sing - ing, I'm sing - ing. I'm glad in ev - ery way. I'm one of God's own chil - dren. He's near me ev - ery day. I'm sing - ing, I'm sing - ing. I'm glad in ev - ery way.

2. I'm clap - ping, I'm clap - ping. I'm glad in ev - ery way. I'm one of God's own chil - dren. He's near me ev - ery day. I'm clap - ping, I'm clap - ping. I'm glad in ev - ery way.

3. I'm march - ing, I'm march - ing. I'm glad in ev - ery way. I'm one of God's own chil - dren. He's near me ev - ery day. I'm march - ing, I'm march - ing. I'm glad in ev - ery way.

I will send rain upon the earth. I Kings 18: 1c.

Raindrops

Marie Pooler

Marie Pooler

Pit-ter, pat-ter, pit-ter, pat-ter, hear the lit-tle rain-drops!

Splash, splash, splash, splash, hear the big rain-drops!

God is send-ing show-ers for the flow-ers and the grass.

God is send-ing show-ers. Pit-ter, pat-ter, splash!

254

Jesus, Lead Me Day by Day

Anonymous

George C. Strattner

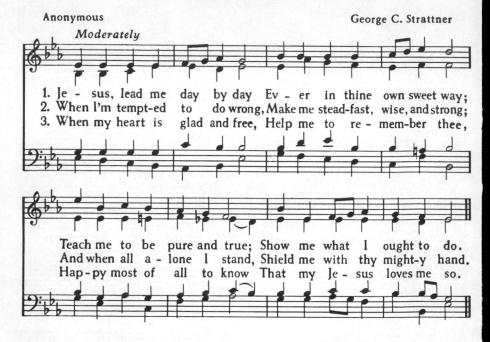

Moderately

1. Je - sus, lead me day by day Ev - er in thine own sweet way;
2. When I'm tempt-ed to do wrong, Make me stead-fast, wise, and strong;
3. When my heart is glad and free, Help me to re - mem-ber thee,

Teach me to be pure and true; Show me what I ought to do.
And when all a - lone I stand, Shield me with thy might-y hand.
Hap-py most of all to know That my Je - sus loves me so.

255

Dear Father in Heaven

Anonymous

J. R. Weber
Harm. Robert Wetzler

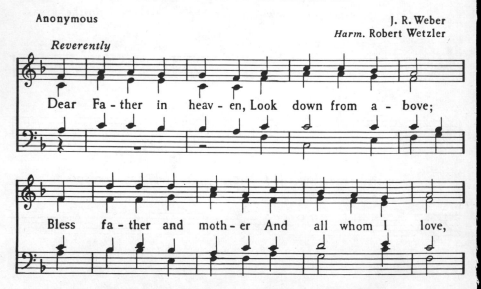

Reverently

Dear Fa - ther in heav - en, Look down from a - bove;

Bless fa - ther and moth - er And all whom I love,

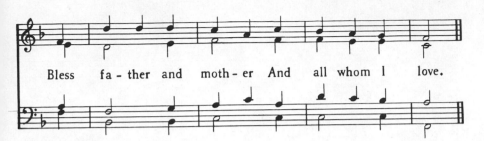

Bless fa - ther and moth - er And all whom I love.

Harmonization copyright Augsburg Publishing House.

My Heavenly Father Loves Me 256

Grace Gabrielsen

Melchior Vulpius

Simply

1. My heaven - ly Fa - ther loves me: Made me to be his own,
2. I'm thank - ful to my Fa - ther For those who show me love,
3. My Je - sus grew as I have. He is my friend to - day.
4. My Je - sus is my Sav - ior; He died, he rose, for me.
5. My God would want that all men Could know his on - ly Son.

Gave me his world to live in, And how to live, I'm shown.
For God's great gift in Je - sus, All given me from a - bove.
He tells me of my Fa - ther And teach - es me to pray.
There - fore I want to wor - ship The Ho - ly Trin - i - ty.
I want to do what I can To help them, ev - ery - one.

RESOURCES FOR WORSHIP

THE LORD'S PRAYER

Our Father, who art in heaven, Hallowed be thy Name, Thy kingdom come, Thy will be done, on earth as it is in heaven. Give us this day our daily bread; And forgive us our trespasses, as we forgive those who trespass against us; And lead us not into temptation, But deliver us from evil. For thine is the kingdom, and the power, and the glory, for ever and ever. Amen.

THE APOSTLES' CREED

I believe in God the Father Almighty, Maker of heaven and earth:
And in Jesus Christ his only Son our Lord, Who was conceived by the Holy Ghost, Born of the Virgin Mary, Suffered under Pontius Pilate, Was crucified, dead, and buried: He descended into hell; The third day he rose again from the dead; He ascended into heaven, And sitteth on the right hand of God the Father Almighty; From thence he shall come to judge the quick and the dead.
I believe in the Holy Ghost; the Holy Christian* Church, the Communion of Saints; The Forgiveness of sins; The Resurrection of the body, And the Life everlasting. Amen.

THE NICENE CREED

I believe in one God, the Father Almighty, Maker of heaven and earth, And of all things visible and invisible.
And in one Lord Jesus Christ, the only-begotten Son of God, Begotten of his Father before all worlds, God of God, Light of Light, Very God of very God, Begotten, not made, Being of one substance with the Father, By whom all things were made: Who for us men, and for our salvation, came down from heaven, And was incarnate by the Holy Ghost of the Virgin Mary, And was made man; And was crucified also for us under Pontius Pilate. He suffered and was buried; And the third day he rose again according to the Scriptures, And ascended into heaven, And sitteth on the right hand of the Father. And he shall come again with glory to judge both the quick and the dead: Whose kingdom shall have no end.
And I believe in the Holy Ghost, The Lord and Giver of Life, Who proceedeth from the Father and the Son, Who with the Father and the Son together is worshipped and glorified, Who spake by the Prophets. And I believe one Holy Christian* and Apostolic Church. I acknowledge one Baptism for the remission of sins. And I look for the Resurrection of the dead, And the Life of the world to come. Amen.

---

*Or, "Holy catholic . . .," *the original and generally accepted text.*

2

Devotions

I

LEADER: In the Name of the Father, and of the Son, and of the Holy Ghost.

RESPONSE: *Amen.*

Lord, have mercy upon us.
Lord, have mercy upon us.
Christ, have mercy upon us.
Christ, have mercy upon us.
Lord, have mercy upon us.
Lord, have mercy upon us.

ALL: THE LORD'S PRAYER *and* THE APOSTLES' CREED.

LEADER: Unto thee have I cried, O Lord:

RESPONSE: *And in the morning shall my prayer come before thee.*

Let my mouth be filled with thy praise:
And with thy honor all the day.
O Lord, hide thy face from my sins:
And blot out all mine iniquities.
Create in me a clean heart, O God:
And renew a right spirit within me.
Cast me not away from thy presence:
And take not thy Holy Spirit from me.
Restore unto me the joy of thy salvation:
And uphold me with thy free Spirit.
Vouchsafe, O Lord, this day:
To keep us without sin.
Have mercy upon us, O Lord:
Have mercy upon us.
O Lord, let thy mercy be upon us:
As our trust is in thee.
Hear my prayer, O Lord:
And let my cry come unto thee.
The Lord be with you.
And with thy spirit.
Let us pray.

3

(Suitable prayers may be offered, after which the following prayer may be offered by the leader:)

We give thanks to thee, heavenly Father, through Jesus Christ, thy dear Son, that thou hast protected us through the night from all danger and harm; and we beseech thee to preserve and keep us, this day also, from all sin and evil; that in all our thoughts, words, and deeds we may serve and please thee. Into thy hands we commend our bodies and souls, and all that is ours. Let thy holy angel have charge concerning us, that the wicked one have no power over us. *Amen.*

LEADER: Bless we the Lord.
RESPONSE: *Thanks be to God.*

ALL: May the Lord Almighty direct our days and our deeds in his peace. Amen.

From THE MORNING SUFFRAGES. Reprinted from the SERVICE BOOK AND HYMNAL, by permission.

4

Devotions

II

OPENING HYMN

INVOCATION

> LEADER: In the Name of the Father, and of the Son, and of the Holy Ghost.
>
> RESPONSE: *Amen.*

OPENING VERSICLES

> I was glad when they said unto me:
> *Let us go into the house of the Lord.*
> O come, let us worship the Lord:
> *For he is our maker.*
> O Lord, open thou my lips:
> *And my mouth shall show forth thy praise.*

PSALM

GLORIA PATRI

> ALL: Glory be to the Father, and to the Son, and to the Holy Ghost: as it was in the beginning, is now, and ever shall be, world without end. Amen.

GOD'S WORD*

OUR RESPONSE FROM THE WORD*

OUR RESPONSE IN SONG*

CLOSING VERSICLES

> LEADER: We praise thee, O God:
> RESPONSE: *We acknowledge thee to be the Lord.*

---

* Refer to listing, page 7 ff.

5

All the earth doth worship thee:
The Father everlasting.
Holy, holy, holy, Lord God of Sabaoth:
Heaven and earth are full of the majesty of thy glory.
Bless we the Father, and the Son, and the Holy Ghost:
We praise and magnify him forever.
O Lord, let thy mercy be upon us:
As our trust is in .thee.
The Lord be with you:
And with thy spirit.
Let us pray.

PRAYER *(The prayer for the season may be used, followed by the Lord's Prayer. The service may close with a hymn.)*

This service is based on A GENERAL ORDER, THE CHRISTIAN YOUTH HYMNAL, *pages 308-309. Used by permission of Muhlenberg Press.*

Devotions

III

This listing is by way of suggestion toward stimulating individual thought in the use of Scripture and song throughout the year. It is not meant to be followed rigidly. Scripture responses may be written on the blackboard for study and perhaps memorization. It would be well to select one appropriate hymn to be emphasized even though others are used at the same service.

God's Word	Our Response from the Word	Our Response in Song
	ADVENT I	
Isaiah 9:6	"Behold, a virgin shall conceive and bear a son, and his name shall be called Emmanuel" (which means, God with us) (Matthew 1:23).	O Come, O Come, Emmanuel 2
	ADVENT II	
Isaiah 40:11	The Lord is my shepherd, I shall not want (Psalm 23:1a).	The Lord's My Shepherd 140
	ADVENT III	
Matthew 11: 2-10	"My soul magnifies the Lord, and my spirit rejoices in God my Savior" (Luke 1:46b-47).	O How Shall I Receive Thee 5
	ADVENT IV	
Psalm 24:7-10	"Blessed is the King who comes in the name of the Lord! Peace in heaven and glory in the highest!" (Luke 19: 38.)	Lift Up Your Heads, Ye Mighty Gates 1

CHRISTMAS DAY

Luke 2:1-7

For to us a child is born, to us a son is given; and the government will be upon his shoulder, and his name will be called "Wonderful Counselor, Mighty God, Everlasting Father, Prince of Peace" (Isaiah 9:6).

Joy to the World   9

CHRISTMAS I

Luke 2:8-12

"Glory to God in the highest, and on earth peace among men with whom he is pleased!" (Luke 2:14.)

Angels We Have Heard on High   19

CIRCUMCISION AND NAME OF JESUS

Luke 2:21

O Lord, our Lord, how majestic is thy name in all the earth! (Psalm 8:1a.)

Jesus, Name of Wondrous Love   194

CHRISTMAS II

John 14:6

Thou dost show me the path of life; in thy presence there is fulness of joy, in thy right hand are pleasures for evermore (Psalm 16:11).

Thy Little Ones, Dear Lord, Are We   30

THE EPIPHANY

Matthew 2: 1-12

O come, let us worship and bow down, let us kneel before the Lord, our Maker! (Psalm 95:6.)

As with Gladness Men of Old   44

EPIPHANY I

Luke 2:41-52

One thing have I asked of the Lord, that will I seek after; that I may dwell in the house of the Lord all the days of my life, to behold the beauty of the Lord, and to inquire in his temple (Psalm 27:4).

O That the Lord Would Guide My Ways   130

EPIPHANY II

Luke 6:35-36

"Blessed are the merciful, for they shall obtain mercy" (Matthew 5:7).

Lord, Speak to Me   175

8

TRINITY VIII

Luke 11:9-10

Those who know thy name put their trust in thee, for thou, O Lord, hast not forsaken those who seek thee (Psalm 9:10).

Breathe on Me, Breath of God 75

TRINITY IX

Luke 15:11-32

As a father pities his children, so the Lord pities those who fear him (Psalm 103:13).

Father Most Holy, Merciful and Tender 80

TRINITY X

Mark 11:15-17

Holiness befits thy house, O Lord, for evermore (Psalm 93:5b).

How Blessed Is This Place 116

TRINITY XI

Luke 18:9-14

He leads the humble in what is right, and teaches the humble his way (Psalm 25:9).

When I Survey the Wondrous Cross 56

TRINITY XII

Matthew 8: 23-27

O give thanks to the Lord, call on his name, make known his deeds among the peoples! (Psalm 105:1).

Beautiful Savior 90

TRINITY XIII

Luke 10:30-37

Love does no wrong to a neighbor; therefore love is the fulfilling of the law (Romans 13:10).

Love Divine, All Loves Excelling 97

TRINITY XIV

Luke 17:11-19

I will give to the Lord the thanks due to his righteousness, and I will sing praise to the name of the Lord, the Most High (Psalm 7:17).

Now Thank We All Our God 190

TRINITY XV

Matthew 6: 25-26

Great is his steadfast love toward us; and the faithfulness of the Lord endures for ever (Psalm 117:2a).

Children of the Heavenly Father 146

TRINITY XVI

Luke 7:11-16

O sing to the Lord a new song, for he has done marvelous things! (Psalm 98:1a).

When Morning Gilds the Skies 95

13

Trinity XVII

Luke 14:7-11	A man's pride will bring him low, but he who is lowly in spirit will obtain honor (Proverbs 29:23).	Take My Life and Let It Be Consecrated 174

Trinity XVIII

Matthew 22: 35-40	I love thee, O Lord, my strength (Psalm 18:1).	Be Thou My Vision 166

Trinity XIX

Matthew 6: 9-13	The Lord has heard my supplication; the Lord accepts my prayer (Psalm 6:9).	Lord, Teach Us How to Pray Aright 159

Trinity XX

Matthew 18: 1-5	Jesus said, "Let the children come to me, do not hinder them; for to such belongs the kingdom of God" (Mark 10:14b).	That Sweet Story of Old 150

Trinity XXI

John 4: 46b-53	I will give thanks to the Lord with my whole heart; I will tell of all thy wonderful deeds (Psalm 9:1).	Praise, My Soul, the King of Heaven 100

Trinity XXII

Matthew 18: 21-22	Forgive us our debts, As we also have forgiven our debtors (Matthew 6:12).	Thy Life Was Given for Me 173

Trinity XXIII

Matthew 22: 15-22	Those who trust in the Lord are like Mount Zion, which cannot be moved, but abides for ever (Psalm 125:1).	Immortal, Invisible, God Only Wise 93

Trinity XXIV

Luke 18:35-43	O give thanks to the Lord, call on his name, make known his deeds among the peoples! (Psalm 105:1).	All Hail the Power of Jesus' Name 91

Trinity XXV

John 14:1-3	Blessed are those who dwell in thy house, ever singing thy praise! (Psalm 84:4.)	In Heaven Above 88

14

TRINITY XXVI

Matthew 25:
34-40

Jesus said, "You shall love the Lord your God with all your heart, and with all your soul, and with all your mind. This is the great and first commandment. And a second is like it, You shall love your neighbor as yourself" (Matthew 22:37-39).

Behold a
Host   86

TRINITY—LAST

Matthew 25:
1-13

I wait for the Lord, my soul waits, and in his word I hope (Psalm 130: 5).

Wake, Awake,
for Night Is
Flying   6

ANNIVERSARY OR DEDICATION

Psalm 84:1-2

I was glad when they said to me, "Let us go to the house of the Lord!" (Psalm 122:1.)

How Blessed
Is This Place 116

NATIONAL

Psalm 22:27-28

Blessed is the nation whose God is the Lord, the people whom he has chosen as his heritage! (Psalm 33: 12.)

God of Our
Fathers   195

MISSIONS

Matthew 28:
18-20

How beautiful upon the mountains are the feet of him who brings good tidings, who publishes peace, who brings good tidings of good, who publishes salvation (Isaiah 52:7a).

I Love to Tell
the Story   124

REFORMATION

Romans 5:1-5

Jesus said, "If you continue in my word, you are truly my disciples, and you will know the truth, and the truth will make you free" (John 8:31-32).

A Mighty
Fortress   185

THANKSGIVING

Psalm 100

It is good to give thanks to the Lord, to sing praises to thy name, O Most High; to declare thy steadfast love in the morning, and thy faithfulness by night (Psalm 92:1-2).

We Praise
Thee, O God 191

15

Psalms

Psalm 1

Blessed is the man who walks not in the counsel of the wicked : nor stands in the way of sinners, nor sits in the seat of scoffers;

But his delight is in the law of the LORD : and on his law he meditates day and night.

He is like a tree planted by streams of water : that yields its fruit in its season,

And its leaf does not wither : in all that he does, he prospers.

The wicked are not so : but are like chaff which the wind drives away.

Therefore the wicked will not stand in the judgment : nor sinners in the congregation of the righteous;

For the LORD knows the way of the righteous : but the way of the wicked will perish.

Psalm 8

O LORD, our Lord, how majestic is thy name in all the earth : thou whose glory above the heavens is chanted by the mouth of babes and infants,

Thou hast founded a bulwark because of thy foes : to still the enemy and the avenger.

When I look at thy heavens, the work of thy fingers : the moon and the stars which thou hast established;

What is man that thou art mindful of him : and the son of man that thou dost care for him?

Yet thou hast made him little less than God : and dost crown him with glory and honor.

Thou hast given him dominion over the works of thy hands : thou hast put all things under his feet,

All sheep and oxen : and also the beasts of the field,

The birds of the air, and the fish of the sea : whatever passes along the paths of the sea.

O LORD, our Lord : how majestic is thy name in all the earth!

Psalm 19

The heavens are telling the glory of God : and the firmament proclaims his handiwork.

Day to day pours forth speech : and night to night declares knowledge.

There is no speech, nor are there words : their voice is not heard;

Yet their voice goes out through all the earth : and their words to the end of the world.

In them he has set a tent for the sun : which comes forth like a bridegroom leaving his chamber, and like a strong man runs its course with joy.

Its rising is from the end of the heavens, and its circuit to the end of them : and there is nothing hid from its heat.

The law of the LORD is perfect, reviving the soul : the testimony of the LORD is sure, making wise the simple;

The precepts of the LORD are right, rejoicing the heart : the commandment of the LORD is pure, enlightening the eyes;

The fear of the LORD is clean, enduring for ever : the ordinances of the LORD are true, and righteous altogether.

More to be desired are they than

gold, even much fine gold : sweeter also than honey and drippings of the honeycomb.

Moreover by them is thy servant warned : in keeping them there is great reward.

But who can discern his errors : clear thou me from hidden faults.

Keep back thy servant also from presumptuous sins; let them not have dominion over me : then I shall be blameless, and innocent of great transgression.

Let the words of my mouth and the meditation of my heart be acceptable in thy sight : O LORD, my rock and my redeemer.

Psalm 23

The LORD is my shepherd : I shall not want;

He makes me lie down in green pastures : he leads me beside still waters;

He restores my soul : he leads me in paths of righteousness for his name's sake.

Even though I walk through the valley of the shadow of death, I fear no evil : for thou art with me; thy rod and thy staff, they comfort me.

Thou preparest a table before me in the presence of my enemies : thou anointest my head with oil, my cup overflows.

Surely goodness and mercy shall follow me all the days of my life : and I shall dwell in the house of the LORD for ever.

Psalm 24

The earth is the LORD's and the fulness thereof : the world and those who dwell therein;

For he has founded it upon the seas : and established it upon the rivers.

Who shall ascend the hill of the LORD : and who shall stand in his holy place?

He who has clean hands and a pure heart : who does not lift up his soul to what is false, and does not swear deceitfully.

He will receive blessing from the LORD : and vindication from the God of his salvation.

Such is the generation of those who seek him : who seek the face of the God of Jacob.

Lift up your heads, O gates! and be lifted up, O ancient doors : that the King of glory may come in.

Who is the King of glory : the LORD, strong and mighty, the LORD, mighty in battle!

Lift up your heads, O gates! and be lifted up, O ancient doors : that the King of glory may come in!

Who is this King of glory : the LORD of hosts, he is the King of glory!

Psalm 27

The LORD is my light and my salvation; whom shall I fear : the LORD is the stronghold of my life; of whom shall I be afraid?

When evildoers assail me, uttering slanders against me, my adversaries and foes : they shall stumble and fall.

Though a host encamp against me, my heart shall not fear : though war arise against me, yet I will be confident.

One thing have I asked of the LORD,

17

that will I seek after : that I may dwell in the house of the LORD all the days of my life, to behold the beauty of the LORD, and to inquire in his temple.

For he will hide me in his shelter in the day of trouble : he will conceal me under the cover of his tent, he will set me high upon a rock.

And now my head shall be lifted up : above my enemies round about me;

And I will offer in his tent sacrifices with shouts of joy : I will sing and make melody to the LORD.

Hear, O LORD, when I cry aloud : be gracious to me and answer me!

Thou hast said, "Seek ye my face" : my heart says to thee, "Thy face, LORD, do I seek."

Hide not thy face from me : turn not thy servant away in anger,

Thou who hast been my help : cast me not off, forsake me not, O God of my salvation!

For my father and my mother have forsaken me : but the LORD will take me up.

Teach me thy way, O LORD : and lead me on a level path because of my enemies.

Give me not up to the will of my adversaries : for false witnesses have risen against me, and they breathe out violence.

I believe that I shall see : the goodness of the LORD in the land of the living!

Wait for the LORD : be strong, and let your heart take courage; yea, wait for the LORD!

Psalm 46

God is our refuge and strength : a very present help in trouble.

Therefore we will not fear though the earth should change : though the mountains shake in the heart of the sea;

Though its waters roar and foam : though the mountains tremble with its tumult.

There is a river whose streams make glad the city of God : the holy habitation of the Most High.

God is in the midst of her, she shall not be moved : God will help her right early.

The nations rage, the kingdoms tot-ter : he utters his voice, the earth melts.

The LORD of hosts is with us : the God of Jacob is our refuge.

Come, behold the works of the LORD : how he has wrought desolations in the earth.

He makes wars cease to the end of the earth : he breaks the bow, and shatters the spear, he burns the chariots with fire!

"Be still, and know that I am God : I am exalted among the nations, I am exalted in the earth!"

The LORD of hosts is with us : the God of Jacob is our refuge.

Psalm 51

Have mercy on me, O God, according to thy steadfast love : according to thy abundant mercy blot out my transgressions.

Wash me thoroughly from my iniq-uity : and cleanse me from my sin!

For I know my transgressions : and my sin is ever before me.

Against thee, thee only, have I sinned, and done that which is evil in

18

thy sight : so that thou art justified in thy sentence and blameless in thy judgment.

Behold, I was brought forth in iniquity : and in sin did my mother conceive me.

Behold, thou desirest truth in the inward being : therefore teach me wisdom in my secret heart.

Purge me with hyssop, and I shall be clean : wash me, and I shall be whiter than snow.

Fill me with joy and gladness : let the bones which thou hast broken rejoice.

Hide thy face from my sins : and blot out all my iniquities.

Create in me a clean heart, O God : and put a new and right spirit within me.

Cast me not away from thy presence : and take not thy holy Spirit from me.

Restore to me the joy of thy salvation : and uphold me with a willing spirit.

Then I will teach transgressors thy ways : and sinners will return to thee.

Deliver me from bloodguiltiness, O God, thou God of my salvation : and my tongue will sing aloud of thy deliverance.

O Lord, open thou my lips : and my mouth shall show forth thy praise.

For thou hast no delight in sacrifice : were I to give a burnt offering, thou wouldst not be pleased.

The sacrifice acceptable to God is a broken spirit : a broken and contrite heart, O God, thou wilt not despise.

Do good to Zion in thy good pleasure : rebuild the walls of Jerusalem,

Then wilt thou delight in right sacrifices, in burnt offerings and whole burnt offerings : then bulls will be offered on thy altar.

Psalm 67

May God be gracious to us and bless us : and make his face to shine upon us,

That thy way may be known upon earth : thy saving power among all nations.

Let the peoples praise thee, O God : let all the peoples praise thee!

Let the nations be glad and sing for joy : for thou dost judge the peoples with equity and guide the nations upon earth.

Let the peoples praise thee, O God : let all the peoples praise thee!

The earth has yielded its increase : God, our God, has blessed us.

God has blessed us : let all the ends of the earth fear him!

Psalm 84

How lovely is thy dwelling place, O Lord of hosts! My soul longs, yea, faints for the courts of the Lord : my heart and flesh sing for joy to the living God.

Even the sparrow finds a home, and the swallow a nest for herself, where she may lay her young : at thy altars, O Lord of hosts, my King and my God.

Blessed are those who dwell in thy house : ever singing thy praise!

Blessed are the men whose strength is in thee: in whose heart are the highways to Zion.

As they go through the valley of

19

Baca they make it a place of springs : the early rain also covers it with pools.

They go from strength to strength : the God of gods will be seen in Zion.

O LORD God of hosts, hear my prayer : give ear, O God of Jacob!

Behold our shield, O God : look upon the face of thine anointed!

For a day in thy courts is better than a thousand elsewhere : I would rather be a doorkeeper in the house of my God than dwell in the tents of wickedness.

For the LORD God is a sun and shield : he bestows favor and honor.

No good thing does the LORD withhold from those who walk uprightly : O LORD of hosts, blessed is the man who trusts in thee!

Psalm 91

He who dwells in the shelter of the Most High : who abides in the shadow of the Almighty,

Will say to the LORD, "My refuge and my fortress : my God, in whom I trust."

For he will deliver you from the snare of the fowler : and from the deadly pestilence;

He will cover you with his pinions, and under his wings you will find refuge : his faithfulness is a shield and buckler.

You will not fear the terror of the night : nor the arrow that flies by day,

Nor the pestilence that stalks in darkness : nor the destruction that wastes at noonday.

A thousand may fall at your side, ten thousand at your right hand : but it will not come near you.

You will only look with your eyes : and see the recompense of the wicked.

Because you have made the LORD your refuge : the Most High your habitation,

No evil shall befall you : no scourge come near your tent.

For he will give his angels charge of you : to guard you in all your ways.

On their hands they will bear you up : lest you dash your foot against a stone.

You will tread on the lion and the adder : the young lion and the serpent you will trample under foot.

Because he cleaves to me in love, I will deliver him : I will protect him, because he knows my name.

When he calls to me, I will answer him : I will be with him in trouble, I will rescue him and honor him.

With long life I will satisfy him : and show him my salvation.

Psalm 93

The LORD reigns; he is robed in majesty : the LORD is robed, he is girded with strength.

Yea, the world is established : it shall never be moved;

Thy throne is established from of old : thou art from everlasting.

The floods have lifted up, O LORD, the floods have lifted up their voice : the floods lift up their roaring.

Mightier than the thunders of many waters : mightier than the waves of the sea, the Lord on high is mighty!

Thy decrees are very sure : holiness befits thy house, O LORD, for evermore.

20

Psalm 100

Make a joyful noise to the LORD, all the lands : serve the LORD with gladness! Come into his presence with singing!

Know that the LORD is God : it is he that made us, and we are his; we are his people, and the sheep of his pasture.

Enter his gates with thanksgiving, and his courts with praise : give thanks to him, bless his name!

For the LORD is good; his steadfast love endures for ever : and his faithfulness to all generations.

Psalm 121

I lift up my eyes to the hills : from whence does my help come?

My help comes from the LORD : who made heaven and earth.

He will not let your foot be moved : he who keeps you will not slumber.

Behold, he who keeps Israel : will neither slumber nor sleep.

The LORD is your keeper : the LORD is your shade on your right hand.

The sun shall not smite you by day : nor the moon by night.

The LORD will keep you from all evil : he will keep your life.

The LORD will keep your going out and your coming in : from this time forth and for evermore.

Psalm 130

Out of the depths : I cry to thee, O LORD!

LORD, hear my voice : let thy ears be attentive to the voice of my supplications!

If thou, O LORD, shouldst mark iniquities : LORD, who could stand?

But there is forgiveness with thee : that thou mayest be feared.

I wait for the LORD, my soul waits : and in his word I hope;

My soul waits for the LORD more than watchmen for the morning : more than watchmen for the morning.

O Israel, hope in the LORD! For with the LORD there is steadfast love : and with him is plenteous redemption.

And he will redeem Israel : from all his iniquities.

Psalm 150

Praise the LORD! Praise God in his sanctuary : praise him in his mighty firmament!

Praise him for his mighty deeds : praise him according to his exceeding greatness!

Praise him with trumpet sound : praise him with lute and harp!

Praise him with timbrel and dance : praise him with strings and pipe!

Praise him with sounding cymbals : praise him with loud clashing cymbals!

Let everything that breathes : praise the LORD! Praise the LORD!

GLORY BE TO THE FATHER, AND TO THE SON, AND TO THE HOLY GHOST : AS IT WAS IN THE BEGINNING, IS NOW, AND EVER SHALL BE, WORLD WITHOUT END. AMEN.

Canticles

Magnificat. Luke 1:46-55

My soul magnifies the LORD : and my spirit rejoices in God my Savior,

For he has regarded : the low estate of his handmaiden.

For behold, henceforth : all generations will call me blessed;

For he who is mighty has done great things for me : and holy is his name.

And his mercy is on those who fear him : from generation to generation.

He has shown strength with his arm : he has scattered the proud in the imagination of their hearts,

He has put down the mighty from their thrones : and exalted those of low degree;

He has filled the hungry with good things : and the rich he has sent empty away.

He has helped his servant Israel, in remembrance of his mercy : as he spoke to our fathers, to Abraham and to his posterity for ever.

Nunc Dimittis. Luke 2:29-32

LORD, now lettest thou thy servant depart in peace : according to thy word;

For mine eyes have seen thy salvation : which thou hast prepared in the presence of all peoples,

A light for revelation to the Gentiles : and for glory to thy people Israel.

Te Deum laudamus

We praise thee, O God : we acknowledge thee to be the LORD.

All the earth doth worship thee : the Father everlasting.

To thee all angels cry aloud : the heavens and all the powers therein.

To thee Cherubim and Seraphim : continually do cry,

Holy, holy, holy : LORD God of Sabaoth;

Heaven and earth are full of the majesty : of thy glory.

The glorious company of the Apostles praise thee : the goodly fellowship of the Prophets praise thee;

The noble army of Martyrs : praise thee.

The holy church throughout all the world doth acknowledge thee: the Father of an infinite majesty;

Thine adorable, true, and only Son : also the Holy Ghost, the Comforter.

Thou art the King of Glory, O Christ : thou art the everlasting Son of the Father.

When thou tookest upon thee to deliver man : thou didst humble thyself to be born of a Virgin.

When thou hadst overcome the sharpness of death : thou didst open the kingdom of heaven to all believers.

Thou sittest at the right hand of God : in the glory of the Father.

We believe that thou shalt come : to be our Judge.

We therefore pray thee help thy servants : whom thou hast redeemed with thy precious blood.

Make them to be numbered with thy saints : in glory everlasting.

O Lord, save thy people and bless thine heritage : govern them and lift them up for ever.

Day by day we magnify thee : and we worship thy name ever, world without end.

Vouchsafe, O Lord : to keep us this day without sin.

O Lord, have mercy upon us : have mercy upon us.

O Lord, let thy mercy be upon us : as our trust is in thee.

O Lord, in thee have I trusted : let me never be confounded.

Benedictus. Luke 1:68-79

Blessed be the Lord God of Israel : for he has visited and redeemed his people,

And has raised up a horn of salvation for us : in the house of his servant David,

As he spoke by the mouth of his holy prophets from of old : that we should be saved from our enemies, and from the hand of all who hate us;

To perform the mercy promised to our fathers : and to remember his holy covenant,

The oath which he swore to our father Abraham : to grant us that we, being delivered from the hand of our enemies, might serve him without fear,

In holiness and righteousness before him : all the days of our life.

And you, child, will be called the prophet of the Most High : for you will go before the Lord to prepare his ways,

To give knowledge of salvation to his people : in the forgiveness of their sins, through the tender mercy of our God,

When the day shall dawn upon us from on high : to give light to those who sit in darkness and in the shadow of death, to guide our feet into the way of peace.

Beatitudes. Matthew 5:3-12

Blessed are the poor in spirit : for theirs is the kingdom of heaven.

Blessed are those who mourn : for they shall be comforted.

Blessed are the meek : for they shall inherit the earth.

Blessed are those who hunger and thirst for righteousness : for they shall be satisfied.

Blessed are the merciful : for they shall obtain mercy.

Blessed are the pure in heart : for they shall see God.

Blessed are the peacemakers : for they shall be called sons of God.

Blessed are those who are persecuted for righteousness' sake : for theirs is the kingdom of heaven.

Blessed are you when men revile you and persecute you and utter all kinds of evil against you falsely on my account : rejoice and be glad, for your reward is great in heaven.

Seasonal Prayers

ADVENT

O holy Child of Bethlehem!
Descend to us, we pray;
Cast out our sin and enter in,
Be born in us today. *Amen.*[1]

CHRISTMAS

O dearest Jesus, Holy Child,
Make thee a bed, soft, undefiled,
Within my heart, that it may be
A quiet chamber kept for thee. *Amen.*[2]

EPIPHANY

O Lord God, who guided the Wise Men to the cradle by the light of a
star and let them see your only-begotten Son; grant that by your grace
we too may see your glory and bring you the gift of our hearts; through
Jesus Christ our Lord. *Amen.*[3]

LENT

O Christ, Lamb of God, who takes away the sin of the world, have
mercy upon us and grant us your peace. *Amen.*[4]

PALM SUNDAY

O blessed Christ, Lord over all, who entered the Holy City in lowly
meekness: teach us by the example of your humility to seek no triumphs
except those which glorify your name. Teach us to crave no honor but
that of following in your way; who livest and reignest with the Father
and the Holy Ghost, ever one God, world without end. *Amen.*[5]

GOOD FRIDAY

Dear Savior, we thank you for giving yourself for us on the Cross of
Calvary. Help us to tell others of the good things you have done for us so
that more people may know that you suffered and died to be the Savior
of all. Teach us to love others as you have loved us, and help us to show
our love in words and actions which are pleasing to you. *Amen.*[6]

EASTER

Dear Lord Jesus, accept our happy songs and our glad praises. We rejoice today in the victory which you won over death and the dark grave by your glorious resurrection. We pray you to live in our hearts so that we may live with you in heaven. *Amen.*[7]

ASCENSION

Dear Lord Jesus, our ascended Savior, we thank you for your loving-kindness and tender mercies toward us. We glory in your return to heaven to prepare a place for us. We pray that we may love you more and serve you better each day of our lives. *Amen.*[8]

PENTECOST

Holy Spirit, divine Comforter, sent into the world to give knowledge of God and understanding of heavenly things, give us a clearer and better understanding of the riches and the power of God and of the way of life which is found in Christ Jesus, our Lord. Take full possession of our minds, and use us for your purposes and service. *Amen.*[9]

TRINITY

Bless us, O God the Father, who has created us; bless us, O God the Son, who has redeemed us; bless us, O God the Holy Spirit, who sanctifies us. O blessed Trinity, keep us in body, soul, and spirit unto everlasting life. *Amen.*[10]

1. *O Little Town of Bethlehem,* hymn No. 27, vs. 4, first half.
2. *From Heaven Above to Earth I Come,* hymn No. 15, vs. 4.
3. German author unknown. Tr., John W. Doberstein: A LUTHERAN PRAYER BOOK, Muhlenberg Press, 1960, p. 91. Altered. Used by permission.
4. Paraphrase of the *Kyrie.*
5. From the CHRISTIAN YOUTH HYMNAL, Muhlenberg Press, 1948, p. 362. Altered. Used by permission.
6. By Katherine Weller and Ella Osten.
7. From the CHILDREN'S HYMNAL AND SERVICE BOOK, Muhlenberg Press, 1929, p. 266. Altered. Used by permission.
8. From the AMERICAN UNIFORM SERIES I, Teachers' Guide. Copyright Augsburg Publishing House.
9. From LUTHERAN BOOK OF PRAYER, Concordia Publishing House, 1951, p. 90. Altered. Used by permission.
10. *Weimarisches Gesangbuch.* From WHEN WE PRAY, Daniel Nystrom, ed., Augustana Book Concern, 1950, p. 142. Altered. Used by permission.

Topical Index

26

27

28

Authors and Sources of Texts

The numbers in parentheses refer to translations or adaptations

Composers and Sources of Tunes

The numbers in parentheses refer to harmonizations,
arrangements, or adaptations

33

INDEX OF TUNES

INDEX

of

TITLES

38